Complete
Sonatas
Part 2

Recent Researches in Music

A-R Editions publishes seven series of critical editions, spanning the history of Western music, American music, and oral traditions.

Recent Researches in the Music of the Middle Ages and Early Renaissance
Charles M. Atkinson, general editor

Recent Researches in the Music of the Renaissance
James Haar, general editor

Recent Researches in the Music of the Baroque Era
Christoph Wolff, general editor

Recent Researches in the Music of the Classical Era
Eugene K. Wolf, general editor

Recent Researches in the Music of the Nineteenth and Early Twentieth Centuries
Rufus Hallmark, general editor

Recent Researches in American Music
John M. Graziano, general editor

Recent Researches in the Oral Traditions of Music
Philip V. Bohlman, general editor

Each edition in *Recent Researches* is devoted to works by a single composer or to a single genre. The content is chosen for its high quality and historical importance, and each edition includes a substantial introduction and critical report. The music is engraved according to the highest standards of production using the proprietary software MusE, owned by MusicNotes, Inc.

For information on establishing a standing order to any of our series, or for editorial guidelines on submitting proposals, please contact:

A-R Editions, Inc.
Middleton, Wisconsin

800 736-0070 (U.S. book orders)
608 836-9000 (phone)
608 831-8200 (fax)
http://www.areditions.com

RECENT RESEARCHES IN THE MUSIC OF THE BAROQUE ERA, 117

Nicola Francesco Haym

Complete Sonatas Part 2

Edited by Lowell E. Lindgren

A-R Editions, Inc.

Middleton, Wisconsin

To Richard Allen Hoglund, Karen Arlene Bowman, and
Kathryn Ann Tompt

Performance parts are available from the publisher.

A-R Editions, Inc., Middleton, Wisconsin
© 2002 by A-R Editions, Inc.

A-R Editions is pleased to support scholars and performers
in their use of *Recent Researches* material for study or performance. Subscribers to any of the *Recent Researches* series,
as well as patrons of subscribing institutions, are invited to
apply for information about our "Copyright Sharing
Policy."

Printed in the United States of America

ISBN 0-89579-504-3
ISSN 0484-0828

♾ The paper used in this publication meets the minimum
requirements of the American National Standard for
Information Sciences—Permanence of Paper for Printed
Library Materials, ANSI Z39.48-1984.

Contents

Acknowledgments

This edition was made possible by the kind cooperation of many fine librarians, scholars, and co-workers, who supplied both basic and cognate source material and information.

I am very grateful to the librarians who sent source material from their collections, answered queries about their holdings, and gave permission for publication of the music and plates found in this edition. At the Library of Congress, they were Charles Sens, Music Specialist, and Kevin LaVine, Music Reference Librarian. At the British Library, they were John Hopson, Archivist, and Andrew Levett of the Division of Music Reproductions. At the British Museum, it was Martin Royalton-Kisch, Assistant Keeper of Flemish Prints and Drawings. At the National Portrait Gallery in London, it was James Kilvington, Assistant Picture Library Manager. At the Bodleian Library in Oxford, they were Peter Ward-Jones, Music Librarian, and Robert J. Bruce, Associate Music Librarian. At Christ Church Library in Oxford, they were John Milsom, Music Specialist, and Janet McMullin, Assistant Librarian. At the Cardiff University Library, it was Gillian Jones, Music Librarian. At the Bibliothèque du Conservatoire Royal in Brussels, it was Paul Raspé, Librarian. At the library of Count Schönborn in Wiesentheid, it was Frohmut Dangel-Hofmann, Bibliothekarische Betreuerin. At the Deutsches Musikgeschichtliches Archiv in Kassel, it was Rainer Birkendorf. At the Conservatorio di Musica "Giuseppe Verdi" in Milan, it was Agostina Zecca Laterza, Librarian. At the Studio Per Edizioni Scelte (S.P.E.S.) in Florence, it was Paola Barocchi, Director.

The following scholars, who are among my good friends, have graciously supplied much information. In alphabetical order, they are Peter Allsop, Paul Atkin, the late Malcolm Boyd, Michael Burden, Paul Corneilson, Anthony DelDonna, Piero Gargiulo, Elizabeth Gibson, Robert D. Hume, Judith Milhous, Curtis Alexander Price, Rudolf Rasch, and Brent Wissick. Dr. Rasch, who is currently completing a study that focuses on the publishing firm of Estienne Roger, has supplied answers to numerous queries about Haym's only publisher, and I am deeply grateful to him for his steadfast help.

The following "specialists" have been my co-workers on this edition: Jeffrey Morrow, M.I.T. class of 1996, John McKay, M.I.T. class of 2000, Mark Ethier, M.I.T. class of 2001, and Lori Holmes, Boston Conservatory class of 2003. John, my chief collaborator, scored all of part 1 and Haym's op. 2 in part 2. His solutions to notational problems were invariably thoughtful and insightful. Jeffrey scored the cello sonatas in part 2. Mark scored the sonata by Gio. Ant. Haym that ends part 2. Lori made the glossy photographs that served as the basis for six of the eight plates.

Christopher Hogwood, director of the Handel and Haydn Society in Boston, provided the impetus for this edition by asking two questions on 2 May 1999, the final day of a Handel conference that he had sponsored. I had made various comments concerning Haym at sessions of the conference, and Hogwood asked first how much of Haym's instrumental music was in print. I said "none," so he then asked why I had not edited any. The next week I ordered copies of Haym's opp. 1 and 2 from both the Library of Congress and the Bodleian Library, then spoke with John McKay, who was looking for an instructive and wage-earning endeavor for the summer. I trust and hope that you will make these hitherto hidden treasures audible to us all.

Introduction

How Londoners "fell in with the Italian" Style "that holds the ear"

Nicola Haym arrived in London in 1701, approximately thirty years after the Neapolitan violinist named Nicola Matteis had settled there.[1] According to the avid amateur Roger North (1651–1734),

> the decadence of the French musick, and the Itallian coming in its room . . . happened by degrees, and the overture was by accident, for the coming over of Sig[r] Nicolai Matteis gave the first start. He was an excellent musitian, and performed wonderfully upon the violin. His manner was singular, but in one respect excelled all that had bin knowne before in England, which was the *arcata*; his *stoccatas, tremolos*, devisions and indeed his whole manner was surprising, and every stroke of his was a mouthfull. Besides all that he played was of his owne composition, which shewed him a very exquisite harmonist, and of a boundless fancy, and invention.

He was at first too proud and high-priced to obtain patronage, and he behaved unfashionably, in that "no person must whisper while he played." Then a few acquaintances showed him how to humor the English; as a result, he had many students and published, between 1676 and 1685, the four parts of his *Ayrs for the Violin* and bass.[2]

Matteis's "teaching, and promiscuous joyning with the English in consort musick and conversation" was the first of "2 circumstances which concurred to convert the English Musick intirely over from the French to the Italian taste." The other

> was the numerous traine of yong travellers of the best quallity and estates, that about this time went over into Italy and resided at Rome and Venice, where they heard the best musick and learnt of the best masters; and as they went out with a favour derived from old Nichola, they came home confirmed in the love of the Itallian manner, and some contracted no litle skill and proved exquisite performers.[3]

As noted in the introduction to part 1, the dedicatees of Haym's opp. 1 and 2 were both at Rome in 1697–98. Wriothesly Russell "came home confirmed in the love of the Itallian manner," while Richard Edgcumbe studied with Corelli, from whom he presumably "contracted no litle skill," then returned to England with a newly painted portrait of his teacher. In 1695, "Giovanni Ravenscroft alias Rederi Inglese" went one step further,

in that he published at Rome his *Sonate a trè*, op. 1. In his address to the reader, he terms it "the first miscarriage of my barren brain, which springs from a dilettante's pen, not a professional's" (il primo aborto del mio sterile ingegno, il quale esce da una penna diletante non professoria).[4] One professional English musician, Robert Valentine (b. 1674), did settle at Rome a few years before Haym left for London.[5]

Even before Matteis arrived in London, "severall litle printed consorts came over from Italy, as Cazzati, Vitali, and other lesser scrapps which were made use of in corners."[6] In other words, printed collections of sonatas written by such composers were sight-read during the 1670s and '80s by ensembles that North played in at "constant and weekly meetings in London." And it was his "fortune to be in that company which introduc't the Itallian composed enterteinements of musick which they call *Sonnata*'s." While the court "entertained" only music that had a "softened and variegated" French air, "wee found most satisfaction in the Italian, for their measures were just and quick, set off with wonderfull solemne *Grave*'s, and full of variety."[7] Henry Purcell was their ally, most notably in his *Sonnatas of III Parts* (1683). In his address to the "Ingenuous Reader," Purcell tells us that he has

> faithfully endeavour'd a just imitation of the most fam'd Italian Masters; principally, to bring the Seriousness and gravity of that Sort of Musick into vogue, and reputation among our Countrymen, whose humor, 'tis time now, should begin to loath the levity, and balladry of our neighbours.

His address concludes by defining the Italian terms found in his score.[8] Since Purcell does not name "the most fam'd Italian Masters," their identity remains unknown; but composers who worked in Rome—such as Lelio Colista and Carlo Ambrogio Lonati—were apparently as "fam'd" in England as those who worked in northern Italy, such as Cazzati, Legrenzi, and Vitali.[9] Around 1695, the year of Purcell's death, North observed: "At length the towne came off the French way, and fell in with the Italian, and now that holds the ear."[10]

Corelli published his op. 1 in Rome during the same year that Purcell published his "New Musical Compositions, called *Sonata*'s,"[11] in London. According to North's reminiscences written at Norfolk during the 1720s (where he had lived since the 1690s), the Italian victory had culminated with the arrival of "Corelly's first consort, that cleared the ground of all other sorts of musick whatsoever. By degrees the rest of his consorts, and at last the conciertos came, all which are to the musitians like the bread of life."[12] "Those became the onely musick relished for a long time. And there seemed to be no satiety of them, nor is the vertue of them yet exhaled, and it is a question whither it will ever be spent, for if musick can be immortall, Corelli's consorts will be so."[13] Thus, Londoners were apparently well acquainted with Corelli's works from ca. 1690 onwards.[14] And when North visited London ca. 1710, he found it "wonderfull to observe what a skratching of Correlli there is every where—nothing will relish but Corelli."[15] Since Haym, as we have described in part 1, edited Corelli's opp. 1–5 for Roger in 1705, and simultaneously helped to edit Corelli's opp. 1–4 for Walsh, he surely aided and abetted this "relish" for his Roman compatriot.

One place where Corelli's works were often "skratched" was the loft above Thomas Britton's coal store in St. John Clerkenwell, London. Britton, a small-coal dealer and amateur musician, acquired an ensemble of musical instruments and a collection of music in order to sponsor a series of Thursday afternoon performances that ran from 1678 until 1714. A note on the title page of one copy of Corelli's op. 1 informs us that "these lessons are in the hand writing of old Thomas Briton, the famous musical Small-coal man, & used at his Assembly for many years."[16] Ned Ward, his neighbor, wittily described "the Small-Coal-Man's Musick Club" in 1709, then appended a poem that includes the lines:

We thrum the fam'd *Corella*'s Aires;
Fine Solos and Sonettos,
New Riggadoons and Maidenfairs,
Rare Jigs and Minuettos.[17]

Britton's collection was sold after his death in 1714, and the sale catalog grouped many hundreds of sets of instrumental parts into 160 numbers. At least forty-four of the numbers contained music by one or more Italian composers. For example, no. 17 had "three printed operas by Vitali, Grossi, and one by divers authors, Italian," no. 21 had "25 Sonatas by Corelli, Bassani, &c. Italian writing," and no. 135 had "Bononcini's Ayres, and a great collection with them."[18] At least sixteen of them contained one or more works by Corelli, whom the British continued to venerate as a "classic" composer throughout and beyond the eighteenth century.[19]

Corelli's op. 5 solo sonatas were printed in Rome in 1700, then by Walsh in London in 1700 and by Roger in Amsterdam in 1702. Walsh entered the competitive world of sonata publications with this volume.[20] Londoners were invited to subscribe for the Roman edition of Corelli's "Twelve Solo's" on 13 April 1699 and were informed on 11 July 1700 that it had arrived in London.[21] Demand must have greatly exceeded supply, because Francis Vaillant advertised a forthcoming edition by Roger on 27 August, Walsh advertised his edition on 29 August, and each claimed that his edition surpassed the other in significant ways.[22]

When Haym and Cosimi arrived in London on 22 March 1701, they thus entered an environment in which the Italian way held sway and the most highly favored opus was the fifth by their Roman friend Corelli. They undoubtedly heard that it was Walsh's first publication of a set of Italian sonatas and observed that his subsequent focus was clearly upon the airs found in chamber sonatas rather than the "free" movements found in church sonatas.[23] On 4 October 1701, for example, he published *Bononcini's Ayres in 3 parts, as Almands, Corrants, Preludes, Gavotts, Sarabands, and Jiggs.*[24] In 1702–3, he reprinted only the airs—i.e., sonatas 7–12—from Corelli's op. 5 in arrangements for flute and continuo and for harpsichord,[25] then reprinted Corelli's chamber sonatas, opp. 2 and 4, which are—according to Walsh's advertisements—Corelli's first and second sets of airs in three parts.[26] On 11 March 1703, he reissued *Sen' Nicola's First and Second Book's of Aire's in 3 Parts, Containing Preludes, Allemand's, Saraband's, Corrant's, Minuett's, and Jigg's, with divers Fancye's and Vollentary's in Every Key for Two Violins and a Bass*: "The Second Treble never being Printed before is now Engraven from the Author's own Manuscript, which renders the whole work Compleat. Composed by Nicola Matteis Napolitano."[27] On 14 August 1703 he issued *Albinoni's Aires in 3 Parts for Two Violins and a Through Bass, Containing Almand's, Saraband's, Corrant's, Gavots, and Jiggs, &c.*[28] On 28 August 1703 he issued *Ziani's* [!] *Aires or Sonatas in 3 Parts for Two Violins and a Thorow-Bass, Containing the Most Refined Italian Aire, op. 1.*[29]

In 1702–3, the two Italian violinists who undoubtedly played Haym's opp. 1–2 with him each published an opus 1 for solo violin and continuo. Their collections may have functioned primarily as a basis for their teaching of aspiring violinists.[30] Nicola Cosimi's twelve *Sonate da camera a violino e violone o cembalo*, op. 1, was engraved at his own expense, was first advertised on 5 November 1702, and was soon "pirated" in an edition by Roger. Each of its sonatas begins with a solemn preludio and continues with three airs: first an allemanda; then a sarabanda or corrente; and finally a giga or gavotta.[31] Gasparo Visconti's six *Sonate a violino e violone o cembalo*, op. 1, published by Roger in Amsterdam, was first advertised in London on 29 April 1703.[32] Walsh "pirated" it on 27 May 1703 with the title *Gasperini's Solos for a Violin with a through Bass for the Harpsicord or Bass Violin, Containing Preludes, Allemands, Sarabands, &c., op. 1.*[33] In the first four sonatas, movements 2 and 4 are allemandes and jigs, respectively. The remaining two works are virtually "free" of airs, because their only binary form is the closing jig in no. 5. No. 6 is clearly the culmination, because it features multiple stops in its second and fourth movements.

Haym, like Visconti, chose Roger rather than Walsh or any other printer.[34] He may have done so because Roger was printing "free" sonatas, as well as airs,[35] because his editions were carefully and elegantly engraved, and because they were distributed in London,[36] as well as on the Continent. Haym's sonatas should have pleased Roger North, because they are "just and quick, set off with wonderfull, solemne *grave*'s, and full of variety." Indeed, they are in every way written for connoisseurs rather than foot-tapping amateurs who sought out collections filled with modern dance airs.[37] Each of his works consists of well-wrought opening movements, contrapuntal second movements (often entitled canzona or allemande), transitional third movements (whose affects will be intensified by improvised embellishments), and a surprising variety of final movements. Op. 2 as a whole is surprising. For example, only the first five of its twelve sonatas are intended exclusively for two violins and continuo, and it ends with its three most extraordinary pieces, two of which place a solo violoncellist on equal footing with a solo violinist. Haym's two solo sonatas for violoncello make their affective points in a very brief span of time, because they were conjecturally written by a teenager who was learning how to compose and play the cello at the same time. The "free" solo sonatas printed in part 1 are far more expansive, and their subtleties require the sensitivities of more experienced musicians. It is not at all surprising that Haym followed not the "airy" trend of the time, but instead wrote intricate music for connoisseurs, because this is congruent with all other aspects of his career. They are summarized in the introduction to part 1 and—far more eloquently and succinctly—in the comprehensive obituary that appeared in *The Weekly Medley* for 9 August 1729:

> He distinguished himself by his indefatigable Industry. . . . Among the many excellent Talents he possess'd, he was deservedly famous for divinely touching the *Violoncello*, or *Four-string Base*, in which he was not equal'd by more than two or three Persons in Europe. It were needless to mention his Genius for Musick as a composer. . . . Notwithstanding his close Application to the above-mention'd Science, he nevertheless devoted several Hours daily to the *Belles-Lettres*, in which he had made a very great Progress. . . . He *design'd* very well, which was of great Service to him in correcting the Plates of his different Works. These great Abilities, heighten'd by an uncommon Modesty, Candour, Affability, and all the amiable Virtues of Life, make all his Friends sincerely regret his Loss.

Five "Free" Sonatas, or *Sonate da chiesa*, in Op. 2, Nos. 1–5

Haym's op. 2, *Sonate a trè, cioè violini, flauti, violoncello e basso continuo per il cembalo*, resembles his op. 1 in that it features the serious affects and contrapuntal textures that characterize the Roman and Corellian tradition(s). Opp. 1 and 2 both specify on their title pages that the basso continuo is for the "cembalo," yet within the part-book itself the instrumental designations "violone" and "o leuto" head alternate pages. Since Haym played the violone, i.e., the violoncello, he presumably conceived his bass lines for it and then wrote the bass figures for a chord-playing instrumentalist. Thus, two instrumentalists should presumably play his bass part. In Haym's day, they would have read from the same score.

In op. 2, only nos. 1–5 have treble parts written exclusively for two violins. They use the minor keys G and A, as well as the major keys C, D, and A. Nos. 6–9, in which the treble parts are apt for two flutes or two violins, bring back the keys of G minor and C major, then introduce the new keys of F major and E minor. Nos. 10–11, in which the "treble" parts are for a violin and a violoncello, restate the key of A minor, then introduce the new key of G major. No. 12, in which the treble parts are designed exclusively for flutes, "recapitulates" the key of G major.[38] As in op. 1, there are thus seven works in major and five in minor keys.

No. 1 in C major opens the collection with boundless energy. The Adagio[39] begins with a stepwise rise from c' to g', which is dramatized by suspensions in leap-frogging violins, then climaxes on g"–f♯"–g". After the stepwise rise is repeated more intensely an octave higher, the climax is repeated within the three-chord transition that ends fourteen slow movements in Haym's op. 1 and fifteen in his op. 2.[40] The ensuing Vivace has a zestful thirteen-note subject that clearly reiterates in condensed form the Adagio's stepwise rise and climax. The exuberance is tempered by a countersubject, which descends chromatically and is played in three-voice imitation during each of the first two expositions (mm. 1–9 and 10–17). The third exposition serves as a transition, which returns (via entries of the subject on E, A, D, and G) to a recapitulation of measures 1–6 in measures 29–34. The ³⁄₂ Adagio in A minor begins with chordal declamation, but soon gives way to a leapfrogging rise from a' to a climax on a" (mm. 5–13), after which it dramatically pauses in measure 14, cadences in the tonic, then moves via a chromatically descending bass to a half cadence. The ensuing ₵ Gavotta is in rounded binary form. The second half begins by restating the opening four-measure phrase in E minor, continues by sequencing downward by fifths an embellished version of measures 1–2, then concludes in measures 24–38 with a recapitulation of the entire first half in the tonic key. In this energetic close, the first phrase is embellished, the second—with its chain suspensions—is extended by one measure, and the third is transformed into a treble hocket with an active bass-line, which is echoed.[41]

No. 2 in D major alternates austere with frolicsome movements. In the ³⁄₄ Largo, an arpeggiated three-note motive is solemnly presented in three-part imitation in measures 1–6; these measures are transposed to the dominant for the rise to the climax in measures 11–16; then they return in the tonic to close the movement in measures 27–32. First-beat suspensions provide rhythmic drive not only in these three expositions, but also in two episodes, which begin with a three-note motive in the bass on beat 2 of measures 6 and 16. The rollicking thirty-note subject of the Allegro recalls the main motive of the preceding Adagio in its notes 2–6 and 8–12. The complete subject is heard three times in the first exposition. In the second (mm. 13–15), it is reduced to twelve notes that include only its head and tail. In the third (mm. 19–26), the violone plays the complete subject in the dominant, then the three parts imitate the twelve-note version in descending fifths (E, A, D). The episodes that follow each exposition consist of two and one-half or three measures of sixteenth-note scales. An echo of the final episode ends with a shocking V^2 chord, a dramatic pause, and a brief Largo, in which a walking bass that somewhat resembles the subject leads to a half cadence. The most austere movement is the $\frac{3}{2}$ Adagio in F-sharp minor, which has long rests (for improvised ornaments?) in measures 1–2, then proceeds with intertwining violins that produce first-beat suspensions over a walking bass. The $\frac{3}{4}$ Vivace is not a dance-like binary form, because it features suspensions and a developmental second half. Pairs of slurred eighth notes, which are heard in the first half only in measure 3, are developed in measures 15–38 of the second in order to provide a "swinging" conclusion.

No. 3 in G minor is by far the most solemn work in the collection. It stresses the plagal or flat side, C minor and its relative major, E-flat, in every movement.[42] The opening Adagio is largely in C minor (mm. 5–16). The subject of the Allegro begins with a C-minor chord, cadences twice in C minor (mm. 12–13 and 17), and cadences twice in E-flat major (mm. 29 and 33–34). E-flat is the key of the $\frac{3}{2}$ Grave. The subject of the closing $\mathbf{c}\frac{3}{4}$ Andante ends in C minor (mm. 1–3), and this movement usually cadences in C minor (mm. 6–7, 9–10, 13–14, 15–16, 22–23, 29–30, and 37–38).

No. 3 begins astringently, with stretto imitation of a dotted note, leaps, syncopations, chromaticism, and, in measures 5–7, a stepwise fall from $\hat{5}$ to $\hat{1}$ in C minor. The opening imitation is then sequenced up a fourth, and the fall is lengthened, as it returns in measures 12–18 with chromatic intensification from $\hat{8}$ to $\hat{1}$ in G minor. The nineteen-note subject of the ensuing canzona begins with a severe dotted-note pattern. It slows to quarters and syncopated half notes after its tenth note, when a twenty-four-note countersubject usurps the listener's attention by means of its rapid eighth and sixteenth notes. Its repeated-note head (comparable to the Beethoven Fifth Symphony motive) is pitted against the dotted-note head of the second through eleventh entries of the subject. The subject is "exposed" six times on the tonic or dominant (mm. 1, 5, 13, 17, 20, and 22), "developed" three times in the mediant or submediant (mm. 27, 29, and 31), and "recapitulated" twice in the tonic (mm. 37 and 41). The violone plays it five times, violin 1 plays it thrice, violin 2 plays it twice, and the two violins share it at the beginning of the recapitulation. The solemn Grave consists of one phrase in E-flat major, plus a three-chord transition to its dominant. By means of a $\mathbf{c}\frac{3}{4}$ time signature and an Andante marking, Haym informs us that the finale is to be played in a sober and detached manner. Unlike the preceding finales, it is a through-composed canzona, not a binary form. The seventeen-note subject is heard thrice in each of the first two expositions (mm. 1 and 10), once in each of the next two (mm. 21 and 28), and thrice in stretto in the last (m. 38). Episodes, which occur after each exposition, are characterized by a sequence of syncopated quarter notes and the Beethoven Fifth motive. The climactic episode is clearly the fourth (mm. 30–37), which rises in pitch, adds

sixteenth notes, and even includes a sequential passage in violin 1 (mm. 34–36) that is rhythmically identical to the forthcoming stretto of the subject (mm. 38–40). Since most of this movement is in C minor, three cadences (in mm. 42, 47, and 52) are needed to establish G minor as the tonic.

No. 4 is a serene piece in the bright key of A major, which contrasts greatly with the severely solemn no. 3. Its opening Adagio maintains a gentle flow by means of a walking bass and leisurely imitation between the violins. The Vivace has a thirteen-note subject, which maintains a smooth eighth-note flow as it is played thrice in each of the three expositions. Slurred pairs of eighths that leap upwards characterize the modulatory episodes and the coda (mm. 8–14 modulate from I to V, mm. 21–24 modulate from V to I, and mm. 31–37 contain the coda). The ensuing Adagio, which is in the tonic key, ascends via gentle imitation from e″ to a climactic a″ in measures 4–5, then via stepwise imitation from a′ to a″ in measures 12–14. The leaping opening of the ¢ Allegro returns to begin the second half in the dominant and to mark the recapitulation in the tonic, which is echoed to close the piece. Imitation and syncopation provide a delectable "swing" to this, the sprightliest movement of the sonata.

No. 5 in A minor ends the first group with a stirring piece, in which the *three* slow movements are laments, while the *three* fast movements are furious. The opening Largo features dotted notes that descend in forceful declamation from $\hat{5}$ to $\hat{1}$, then descends by leap from $\hat{5}$ to $\hat{1}$ in the imitative violins. In the ensuing $\mathbf{c}\frac{3}{4}$ Presto, violin 1 plays eighth-note arpeggios over a chordal accompaniment, which is a texture hitherto found only in the movement added before the finale of op. 1, no. 12. Its first three sections end with "angry" multiple stops in violin 2, and the final section ends with a quiet coda. Violin 1 repeats the opening two bars at the beginnings of sections 2 and 4 (mm. 10–11 and 33–34) and repeats the middle of section 2 at the beginning of section 3 (cf. mm. 15–19 and 23–27). The brief $\mathbf{c}\frac{3}{2}$ Adagio is a quiet lament that should be intensified by embellishments played during the rests in measures 1–5 and 8. The Vivace is a canzona in which the expositions move in eighths and the episodes move in sixteenths, and it should probably sound no less furious than the $\mathbf{c}\frac{3}{4}$ Presto. Its twenty-note subject is played thrice in each of the four expositions (mm. 1, 9, 15, and 20). During the third one, the harmonic movement down by fifths (D, G, C) prepares for the concealed return of the subject in A minor (violin 2 in m. 20). Even though the ensuing Adagio features the dulcet sound of violins moving in parallel thirds over a walking bass, their melodic lines repeatedly descend in the key of D minor, so the affect is sorrowful. Like the other two fast movements, the closing Allegro should sound furious. Within it, Haym intermingles triplets with dotted eighth plus sixteenth pairs. Why did he not write this movement in $\frac{12}{8}$, as he wrote the jigs in op. 1, nos. 11–12? Did he want the dotted rhythms to be attacked far more sharply than they would be in $\frac{12}{8}$ meter? A slightly ornamented recapitulation of measures 1–7 begins on the last beat of measure 15.

Four "Airs," or *Sonate da camera,* in Op. 2, Nos. 6–9

According to the table of contents printed at the end of each partbook, op. 2, nos. 6–9 are "proprie per due Violini o per due Flauti." Haym did not add "traversi," but transverse flutes as well as recorders and violins are presumably welcome to play his treble parts.[43] These chamber sonatas include an adagio, an allemanda, an adagio or grave, and a distinctive finale, which is a fugal canzona in no. 6, a gigue-like gavotta in no. 7, a giga followed by a gavotta in no. 8, and a giga in no. 9. As in op. 1, an allemanda is customarily paired with a giga.

No. 6 in G minor is the first in op. 2 to repeat an earlier key.[44] It differs greatly from no. 3 in G minor, because it does not focus at all on the "plagal" key of C minor, on chromatic intervals, or on other astringent elements. Its slow movements declaim quietly, while its fast ones drive ferociously onward. In the opening Adagio, four elements combine to convey a declamatory flow: the two violins or flutes intertwine, the bass walks steadily, suspensions on the strong beats provide rhythmic impetus, and the movement cadences only at its end (mm. 8–9). The same contrapuntal elements give great impetus to the ensuing Allemanda. Each section cadences after ten measures, but the motion does not stop until the end of each one. The Grave begins on an E-flat chord, then declaims briefly in C and G minor before ending with a half cadence on D. Although the ensuing Allegro is a fugal canzona rather than a binary-form jig, it—like the jig—is in $\frac{6}{8}$ meter. It resembles all of the previous movements in that its cadential structure is distinctive. Its first six expositions each end with half cadences in G or D minor (mm. 6, 14, 18, 25, 30, and 37). Only at the end of the seventh exposition, which ends the movement, does it arrive at a full cadence in the tonic key. Because of its constant eighth notes, its rhythmic vigor equals that of movement 2.[45]

Perhaps because many flutists and violinists were amateurs, the next three sonatas are far simpler in terms of texture and form. No. 7 in C major, which uses the key of no. 1, is a serene sonata with crystal-clear structures. Its opening Adagio features two trebles over a walking bass. Treble 1 rises stepwise from c" through a cadence in measure 3 to c"' in measure 6. It then falls stepwise through a cadence in measure 8 to c" in measure 11. A recapitulation ensues (cf. mm. 1–2 with 11–13), after which the trebles resolve their contrapuntal tension by playing parallel thirds. Parallel thirds continue throughout the Allemanda, in which the basic motive consists of three beats preceded by an upbeat of two sixteenth notes. A rich, chordal texture is produced, because all three parts play sixteenths and eighths. At least one treble part stresses the second beat throughout the $\frac{3}{2}$ Adagio in A minor. Its opening four-measure unit is

immediately sequenced up a fifth, and it returns at the original pitch level in measures 17–20. The merry closing movement of four plus four measures in $\frac{2}{2}$ meter is—like the $\frac{2}{2}$ finales of nos. 1 and 8—aptly entitled Gavotta. Yet its triplets convert it sonically into a $\frac{12}{8}$ jig.

No. 8 in F major opens with stern chordal declamation in a $\frac{3}{4}$ Adagio. In the Allemanda, treble 1 plays a jaunty two-measure motive, then elaborates upon it, which relegates its co-workers to an accompanying function. In the second half, it restates the motive in the dominant and tonic keys, then "permits" treble 2 to join in parallel thirds during the coda. Such thirds, plus a walking bass, provide a smooth cushion for the expressive Adagio in D minor, and they are also frequent in the flowing $\frac{12}{8}$ Giga, which shocks the listener by ending with an echoed phrase in F minor (rather than major).[46] A brief, but merry, fifth movement in F major corrects the "wrong turn." This $\frac{2}{2}$ Gavotta of four plus four measures is the only movement in op. 2 that is marked Da Capo at the end. This presumably calls for its repetition rather than a repetition of the Giga.

No. 9 in E minor begins with a declamatory Adagio that increases in intensity as it proceeds. In the Allemanda, the trebles begin with the jocund motive of two sixteenths plus an eighth note, then frolic in thirds until the coda. The brief $\frac{3}{2}$ Adagio is chordal, and embellishments should be added during the rests in its first three measures. The flowing $\mathbf{C}\frac{12}{8}$ Giga features trebles in parallel thirds. They rise thrice to the dominant during the first half. In the second half, they fall gradually to the tonic, then echo the fall.

Three Extraordinary "Airs" in Op. 2, Nos. 10–12

In nos. 10 and 11, a solo violoncellist supplants the second violinist. This new soloist—originally Haym—occasionally doubles or ornaments the violone/lute/cembalo part, but customarily plays an independent line that interacts motivically with the violinist. No. 10 in A minor is a recondite piece, filled with inexplicable surprises, and is therefore difficult to perform. No. 11 in G major (the only key Haym used twice in both op. 1 and op. 2) is, by comparison, suavely elegant and flowing (see plates 1 and 2).

No. 10 begins with an exceedingly "grave" phrase, which gives way to one that is imitated and much more animated. The movement cadences first in the tonic, then in the dominant key (m. 8). Its second half consists of four animated phrases, each of which is based on a different motive. Imitation occurs most conspicuously as cadences are approached, and for three of them Haym requested dynamic contrasts that appear nowhere else in his op. 1 or op. 2. When a group of four or six eighth notes is repeated, it is marked piano, and each of these brief echoes is followed by a forte cadence (mm. 8–10, 13–14, and 16–17). The "grave" Allemanda that follows is aptly marked Andante (rather than Vivace or Allegro). It features motivic imitation between the violinist and violoncellist. After the second half returns to the tonic key, the cello unexpectedly plays a virtuosic sequence of thirty-second notes, then echoes it. A remarkably similar display of cellistic virtuosity ends the second movement of the first solo sonata printed in part 1 of this edition, and a condensed display will end the final movement of this sonata.

The lyrical ³⁄₂ Adagio in C major features a gentle imitation of slurred quarter notes that descend stepwise. In measures 13–18, an agitated imitation of nonslurred, leaping quarters, underpinned by dissonance on every strong beat, leads to the recapitulation. After the soloists reach the tonic in measure 32, they play calm parallel tenths, echo them, then atypically add a forte closing phrase. The rambunctious ¹²⁄₈ Giga begins with conspicuous leaps in the cello, which are first repeated for an unprepared and unexpected sequence in the relative major in measure 3. The first half ends with patterned figurations in the cello (mm. 9–13), forte cadences that resemble the close of the opening motive (mm. 10–11 and 13–14), and an abrupt arpeggio. The second half ends with more elaborate figuration for the cello (mm. 27–29 and 31–33), with recapitulations of the entire opening motive (mm. 30–31 and 34–35), and with an arpeggio that is extended and terminated by the violoncello. The returns of material from measures 1–2 at the end of each section are meant to be shocking, and all except the final echo should be attacked zestfully.[47]

No. 11 in G major begins with a flowing Adagio, in which slurred pairs of sixteenth notes and unhurried imitative entries continue throughout, and greatly reduce the contrast between the three motives (mm. 1, 4, and 10). Texturally, the motives increase in "sweetness," from none to some to nothing but parallel tenths and thirteenths between the solo parts. The ensuing movement is the slowest Allemanda in Haym's opp. 1–2, for it is marked Largo e Puntato, i.e., quite slow and spiccato, as shown on plates 1–2. Its constant sixteenths provide an underlying flow, while the placement of thirty-second-note pairs distinguishes one motive from another (a in m. 1, b in m. 4, and b' in m. 6). The rhythmic and textural climaxes occur in measures 14–16, which are echoed, after which the flow vanishes into the "ether." The third and last movement consists of a ³⁄₄ Vivace in binary form and a written-out ornamentation of it. Each section is based upon the rhythmic motive introduced by the cello in its opening measure, and the cheerful affect is maintained through the hemiola cadence at the end.

A four-measure phrase and twenty-four written-out variations on it constitute no. 12, the "Partite di Ciaccona" in G major, written specifically for two flutes and bass. It undoubtedly represents obeisance to the tradition of Corelli, because his op. 2, no. 12, is a ciacona in C³⁄₄ that consists of a four-measure phrase and twenty-nine written-out variations upon it. The chordal texture of the four-measure theme is animated differently in each of the twenty-four variations. They retain freshness partly by modulating from G major (theme and vars. 1–4) to E minor (vars. 5–10), C major (vars. 11–19), D minor (var. 20), and G major (vars. 21–24). Progress is halted in the final variation,

where the first six chords are followed by rests under a fermata (which presumably calls for a cadenza-like ornament) and the last six are marked Adagio.

Two "Free" Cello Sonatas by Haym and Two Movements by Quirino

Haym's first extant "essays" in composition, which were conjecturally written when he was about sixteen years of age, are his two known cello sonatas. They survive in a Roman manuscript of the 1690s, in which the name "Nicola Haim" appears twice, namely, at the head of two slow-fast-slow-fast groups of movements. Then "Quirino" appears at the head of a final slow-fast pair. The term *Fine*, which appears three times, serves to confirm that the manuscript includes three works, none of which is titled. Since the two pieces by Haym have the traditional four-movement format, they are presumably sonatas. The first one is tonally exceptional, because it consists of a pair of movements in A minor and a pair in E minor. Whether Quirino Colombani's piece is complete or incomplete will become known only if it is found in a second source. It is printed after Haym's sonatas in this edition.

Sonata no. 1, which is in A minor/E minor, alternates soothing slow movements with fierce fast ones. In its opening Adagio, ominous double stops with suspensions (mm. 1–4) and suavely sequenced dialogues (mm. 5–6 and 8–9) are written into the solo part to give the effect of trio texture. The ³⁄₄ Allegro assai in A minor is a propulsive canzona, in which the twelve-note subject thrice returns in the dominant minor or its relative major before it returns in the tonic (mm. 1, 7, 11, 16, and 21). Only the final statement is followed by a twelve-note "consequent phrase" that brings the melody back to the tonic note, and this "consequent" is echoed. The ³⁄₂ Adagio in E minor begins and ends in ³⁄₂ meter. In between are two six-measure phrases that feature sorrowful, slurred, stepwise descents. The affect of the closing binary-form Presto in E minor is stormy, because relentless sixteenth-note patterns in the cello and repeated eighth notes in the continuo pause only for the cadence that ends the first half.

Sonata no. 2 is in G major, an excellent key for strings and the key most frequently found in Haym's sonatas. This is his only sonata in which the first three movements *all* end with an authentic cadence followed by transitional chords. The opening Adagio consists of a brief lyrical outburst in double stops over a walking bass. The binary-form Allegro begins with a twenty-eight-note subject stated twice in succession, first in the solo part, then in the continuo. The second half begins by stating the subject's first nine notes in the dominant key, by embellishing its continuation, then by stating its final eleven notes in the tonic (mm. 15–16). The continuo remains very active until the closing phrase (mm. 17–20), which is only partly echoed, because the closing cadence is replaced by four transitional chords and a fermata. The second Adagio is in E minor, and—like the first—is a brief flourish with double stops in the solo part. The ¢ Presto assai in binary form begins with imitation that makes it sound as if the two parts are chasing each other.

This continues throughout, even when they play in two- or three-part textures for the cadences in measures 6–9, 11–12, and 17–18.

The manuscript concludes with two movements in G minor by Quirino Colombani. According to a biographical sketch by Giuseppe Ottavio Pitoni (1657–1743), Quirino was born in Correggio, near Reggio Emilia, about 1670 and studied in Rome with Giovanni Bicilli, *maestro di cappella* at the Chiesa Nuova. He served there as *vice-maestro*, then in Ronciglione as *maestro*, before he ventured forth to many cities, including Naples and Modena. He was back in Rome between 1692 and 1698, when he played as a free-lance cellist at events sponsored by Cardinal Ottoboni,[48] and he composed thirteen oratorios while residing in Rome during the years 1695 to 1709.[49] He resumed his post as *maestro di cappella* in Ronciglione shortly before he—"a high-spirited, talented and obliging young man" (giovine di molto spirito e talento e di prontezza nell'operare)—became ill from the exertions of hunting, etc., and died on 6 January 1711.[50] His only known movements from trio sonatas are two transitional third-movement adagios that survive in the manuscript listed as Source D in the critical report, because it also contains the trio sonata by Giovanni Antonio Haym that is printed in this volume.[51] Quirino's only known four-movement "free" sonata for cello is in G major.[52] The Largo in G minor in this edition is in binary form, with a motivic solo part and a walking bass. It thus has the leisurely character of an opening movement, not the transitional character of a third movement. The Minuetto was a modern dance at the time and thus has the character of a closing movement. Perhaps these two movements were considered a complete work. Since Quirino was about a decade older than Haym, he may have given Haym some lessons. If so, this manuscript might contain some "polished" examples of their approach to composition and performance around 1694.

Torsos and Lost Works

Since Haym was an active chamber musician in Rome from about 1694 until 1700 and in London from 1701 until at least 1717, it seems likely that he wrote quite a few pieces in addition to those printed in the two volumes of this edition, but only three torsos survive. Two are preludes by "Hyme" that Walsh printed in *Select Preludes & Vollentarys for the Violin* (January 1705), pages 7 and 30, then in *Select Preludes and Vollentarys for the Flute* (November 1708), pages 4 and 9. According to their title pages, these collections were "made and contrived for the improvement of the hand, with variety of compositions by all the greatest masters in Europe for that instrument."[53] The first prelude contains fifteen measures in F major, while the second has nineteen measures in D minor for the violin and in G minor for the flute. No tempos are given, but both are fast movements that require great skill, because they move in constant sixteenth notes through a wide range. The violin version encompasses the two and a half octaves from a to d'''. The flute version covers nearly two octaves, from f' to

e♭'''. Both are conjecturally second movements from solo sonatas for violin and continuo, written for performances given by Haym with Cosimi or Visconti in London.

The third is the "fluto primo" part for *A New Sonata for Two Flutes by Sign' Haim*, who is identified on the title page of the collection as "Nicolini Haym." The page containing the "fluto primo" part is reproduced in this volume as plate 4.[54] The opening ¢ Adagio is a lyrical movement in which flute 2 (and the bass part, if there was one) would have imitated flute 1. The extant part clearly dominates the ¾ Corent. The brief Adagio that follows was apparently chordal in texture. Each half of the ⅜ finale consists of ten measures that rise and fall stepwise by a fifth in one key, followed by four measures that cadence a fifth higher or lower.

At present, the only known source that lists any additional instrumental piece(s) by Haym is the commonplace book of the composer Johann Sigismund Kusser (1660–1727), who was in London from Christmas 1704 until 29 May 1707, when he left for Dublin.[55] Kusser listed concertos by Haym on two pages: "Concerto Nic. Haym. Partitura" on page 201, "15. Conc. de *Pirro* à 4 Instr. N. Haym" on page 447, and "36. Conc: à 1 Ob.: e 3 Istr. N. Haym" on page 447. The "concerto" from *Pyrrhus and Demetrius* is presumably the "Overture in Pyrrhus, Compos'd by Sig' Nicolini Haym," which was printed in four-part score at the beginning of *Songs in the New Opera of Pyrrhus and Demetrius* (London, [1709]).[56] The "conc." for one oboe and three other instruments is unknown. If the "conc." listed on page 201 is not the same as one of the two on page 447, it is likewise unknown.

One "Free" Sonata by [Gio.] Antonio Haym with Archlute Solos

The only known piece of instrumental chamber music by a Haym other than Nicola is a trio sonata in C major by Giovanni Antonio, who was conjecturally his elder half-brother. The scoring of this work is distinctive, because a second bass part is written for the archlute, which plays soloistically in the fast movements. The brief opening movement is marked Allegro for three pairs of repeated chords, then Adagio for a cadence and a transition. The ensuing Allegro is in ritornello form, in which the ensemble plays four ritornellos (mm. 1–7, 11–15, 20–25, and 31–37), the archlute plays three intervening solos, and the ensemble plays the coda and its echo (mm. 38–45). The following Adagio consists of a series of suspensions. The archlute does not have independent solos in the closing ⅜ Allegro, but it does ornament the bass line in order to respond to one-measure motives played sequentially by the violins.

Notes on Performance

As in part 1, many of the editor's thoughts concerning the proper affect, speed, articulation, ornamentation, and location of the structural climax of a movement are given in the foregoing analyses and in the impending discussion of editorial methods. The "Notes on Performance" in part 1 comment on the meanings of "foreign words" found in both op. 1 and op. 2 by Haym. The brief notes given here will concern the Italian versus the English way of holding the violin and cello around 1700 and Roger North's description of the structure and character of a sonata.

Vignettes that depict precisely how a cellist and a violinist held their instruments when Haym was twenty-one years old are printed in Giuseppe Jacchini's *Concerti per camera a violino e violoncello solo, e nel fine due sonate a violoncello solo col basso* (Modena, 1697).[57] The violin appears to rest on the shoulder, while the pegbox appears to be at waist level. The cello rests (without an endpin) on the floor and is held upright, away from the body, but apparently resting on the left knee. A cherub holds a cello in the same way on the frontispiece to Nicola Cosimi's *Sonate da camera a violino e violone o cembalo* (London, 1702),[58] as does "il virtuoso del Sig^r de Bacqueville" in a Roman caricature of around 1720.[59] If these depictions represent an ideal way to hold and bow the cello, Haym's posture and performance practice may have been essentially the same. Since he was the first Italian cellist to play or settle in London,[60] it is not surprising that he became "deservedly famous for divinely touching the *Violoncello, or Four-string Base,*" or that his obituary writer believed him to be among the best three or four cellists in Europe. He may thus have served as a model for aspiring English cellists, many of whom had undoubtedly learned to play the gamba.[61]

The first Italian violinist who served as a model for the English was Matteis. According to North, "he was a very robust and tall man, and having long armes, held his instrument almost against his girdle," or "against his short ribbs. . . . His bow was long as for a base violl, and he touched his devision with the very point; and I have found very few that will beleeve it possible he could performe as he did in that posture. . . . Out of that awkwardness, he taught the English to hold the bow by the wood onely and not to touch the hair, which was no small reformation."[62]

Objections to this "Italian" manner are made in John Lenton, *The Gentleman's Diversion, or The Violin Explained* (December 1693), which reappeared as *The Useful Instructor on the Violin* (March 1702).[63] Lenton was a member of the twenty-four violins at court from 1681 until his death in 1719, and he also played at the theater, for which he wrote at least twelve suites for plays produced between 1682 and 1705.[64] Therefore, his treatise should crisply capture the English way of playing. Only one copy of it is known to survive. It dates from 1693 and contains the following advice under the heading "Of ordering the Bow and Instrument":[65]

> As I would have none get a habit of holding an Instrument under the Chin, so I would have them avoid placing it as low as the Girdle, which is a mongrel sort of way us'd by some in imitation of the *Italians,* never considering the Nature of the Musick they are to perform; but certainly for *English* Compositions, which generally carry a gay lively Air with them, the best way of commanding the Instrument will be to place it something higher than your Breast, your Fingers round and firm in stopping, not bending your joynts inward, and when you make a Shake let it be from the motion of the Finger alone, and not from any Squeeze of the Body or Wrist (except) it be a close Shake which is done by the consent and operation of all the Fingers; let your Bow be as long as your Instrument, well mounted and stiff Hair'd, it will otherwise totter upon the String in drawing a long stroke; hold it with your Thumb half under the Nutt, half under the Hair from the Nutt, and let it rest upon the middle of the first joynt, place all your Fingers upon the Bow, pretty close, (or for the better guiding of it) you may place the out-side of the first joynt of the little Finger against the Wood, let the Bow move always within an inch of the Bridge directly forward and backward, let your Bow-wrist move loosly, (but not much bent), and hold not up your Elbow, more than necessity requires: Stand or Sit upright, beware of unseemly actions, &c.[66] The Time you beat let it be to your self, unless in Consort you are desired by the rest of the company. With men of Reason I question not but what I have said will appear of use, but if there are any such, who admire the *Italian* manner in *English* performances, they spoil that which (in it self,) is the best manner in the World, to make their own ridiculous.

In closing, one of Roger North's incisive descriptions of the characteristic temperament of each movement of an eloquent *sonata da chiesa,* or "free" sonata, will be cited,[67] because it applies to Haym as well as it does to Corelli and other fine performers. A good performance will successfully convey the special mood and character of each movement. The opening movement has

> all the fullness of harmony figurated and adorned that the master at that time could contrive, and this is termed *grave,* and sometimes, but as I take it, not so properly, *adagio.*[68] . . . This *grave* most aptly represents seriousness and thought. The movement is as of one so disposed, and if he were to speak, his utterance would be according, and his matter rationall and arguing. The upper parts only fulfill the harmony, without any singularity in the movement; but all joyne in a comon tendency to provoke in the hearers a series of thinking according as the air invites, whether Magnifick or Querolous, which the sharp or flat key determines.[69]

The second movement represents the result, or culmination, of all the thinking heard in the first. According to North, after this "Magnifick or Querolous" pondering,

> the parts fall to action, and move quick; and the entrance of this denouement is with a *fuge.*[70] . . . This hath a cast of business or debate, of which the melodious point is made the subject; and accordingly it is wrought over and under till, like waves upon water, it is spent and vanisheth, leaving the musick to proceed smoothly, and as if it were satisfyed and contented.

The shortest movement is the third, and it is declamatory in a chordal manner and/or lyrical in a motivic manner. According to North, the overwhelming affect of this slow movement will cause listeners to react by

> laying all affaires aside, and lolling in a sweet repose: which state the musick represents by a most tranquill but full harmony, and dying gradually, as one that falls asleep.

This movement thus serves as a buffer between the "rationall and arguing" pair that opens the work and the lighthearted movement(s) that are heard after the "Action is resumed." North's description of the closing "Action" names the dances that are found in Haym's finales and in his *sonate da camera*. It also names the ricercata (ricercar) and the andante; as we have seen, they are sometimes found in Haym's final movements, but are far more characteristic of his second movements.

Action is resumed, and the various humors of men diverting themselves (and even their facetiousness and witt) are represented, as the master's fancy at that time invites, wherein the instrument or ingredient of the connexion with humane life is (sometimes the touch or breaking, but cheifly) the measure; as a *gavott*, which is an old French dance; and so *minuets, courants*, and other dancing expressions. There is often the *andante*, which is an imitation of walking *equis passibus* [with equal steps]; there is a *ricercata*, which is to imitate a looking about as for a thing lost; and divers imitations of men's humours well knowne to the performers, so need not be described, and for the most part concluding with a *gigue* which is like men (half foxed) dancing for joy, and so good night.[71]

Notes

1. Haym probably did not meet him, since Matteis probably died in the 1690s. See *The New Grove Dictionary of Music and Musicians*, 2d ed. (hereafter *NG2*), s.v. "Matteis, Nicola (i)," by Peter Walls, and Simon Jones, "The Legacy of the 'Stupendious' Nicola Matteis," *Early Music* 29 (2001): 553–68.

2. Roger North, *On Music, being a Selection from His Essays Written during the Years c.1695–1728*, ed. John Wilson (London: Novello, 1959), 355–58; cited also in *Roger North's "The Musicall Grammarian 1728,"* ed. Mary Chan and Jamie C. Kassler (Cambridge: Cambridge University Press, 1990), 268–71. Three of the English gentlemen "who influenced him to lay aside his Italian behaviour" are named in a passage cited in *Roger North's Cursory Notes of Musicke (c.1698–c.1703): A Physical, Psychological and Critical Theory*, ed. Mary Chan and Jamie C. Kassler (Kensington, Australia: Unisearch Ltd., 1986), 285 n. 213(2).

3. North, "Notes of Comparison between the Elder and Later Musick and Somewhat Historicall of both" (ca. 1726), in *On Music . . . c.1695–1728*, 307–10. Examples are given in Michael Tilmouth, "Music and British Travellers Abroad, 1600–1730," *Source Materials and the Interpretation of Music: A Memorial Volume to Thurston Dart*, ed. Ian Bent (London: Stainer & Bell, 1981), 358–69.

4. Ravenscroft's address has been reprinted in Claudio Sartori, *Bibliografia della musica strumentale italiana stampata in Italia fino al 1700* (Florence: Leo S. Olschki, 1952), 585. The opening themes for this and Ravenscroft's only other publication are given in Fritz Zobeley, *Die Musikalien der Grafen von Schönborn-Wiesentheid: Thematisch-bibliographischer Katalog*, part 1, *Das Repertoire des Grafen Rudolf Franz Erwein von Schönborn (1677–1754)*, vol. 1, *Drucke aus den Jahren 1676 bis 1738* (Tutzing: Hans Schneider, 1967), 92–93. Ravenscroft's op. 1 was reprinted as Corelli's op. 7 by Le Cène at Amsterdam around 1735. It is much like Corelli, though significantly more formulaic, according to Sergio Durante, "Ancora del 'vero' e 'falso' Corelli: Un confronto con i movimenti fugati di Ravenscroft," in *Studi corelliani 4: Atti del quarto congresso internazionale, Fusignano, 4–7 September 1986*, ed. Pierluigi Petrobelli and Gloria Staffieri, Quaderni della Rivista italiana di musicologia, vol. 22 (Florence: L. S. Olschki, 1990), 275–301, and William S. Newman, "Ravenscroft and Corelli," *Music & Letters* 38 (1957): 369–70.

5. *NG2*, s.v. "Valentine, Robert," by Martin Medforth. Valentine published thirteen collections of sonatas, aires, and balletti between 1708 and 1735. They are preclassical in style: "simple, tuneful, well-made and almost uniformly insipid in effect" according to H. Diack Johnstone, "Music in the Home I," in *Music in Britain: The Eighteenth Century*, ed. H. Diack Johnstone and Roger Fiske (Oxford: Basil Blackwell, 1990), 174.

6. North, *On Music . . . c.1695–1728*, 302, 302 n, and 351.

7. North, "As to Musick . . ." (ca. 1695), in *On Music . . . c.1695–1728*, 24–25.

8. His address has been reprinted together with related documents (including comments by Roger North) in Michael Burden, *Purcell Remembered* (London and Boston: Faber and Faber, 1995), 35–42.

9. See Graham Dixon, "Purcell's Italianate Circle," and Peter Holman, "Consort Music," in *The Purcell Companion*, ed. Michael Burden (London and Boston: Faber and Faber, 1995), 38–51 and 281–89, respectively. See also Michael Tilmouth and Christopher D. S. Field, "Consort Music II: from 1660," in *Music in Britain: The Seventeenth Century*, ed. Ian Spink (Oxford: Basil Blackwell, 1992), 264–66. The best surveys of chamber music in England during the decades before Haym's arrival are found in this article by Tilmouth and Field and in Tilmouth, "Chamber Music in England, 1675–1720" (Ph.D. diss., Christ's College, Cambridge, 1959).

10. North, *On Music . . . c.1695–1728*, 25.

11. *London Gazette* for 1–5 November 1683, cited in Burden, *Purcell Remembered*, 40.

12. North, *On Music . . . c.1695–1728*, 310–11. A "consort" is a collection of sonatas.

13. Ibid., 358; and *Roger North's "The Musicall Grammarian 1728,"* 272.

14. His opp. 2–4 were first published in Rome in 1685, 1689, and 1694. In *Harmonia Sacra: Or, Divine Hymns and Dialogues*, Book II (1693), Corelli's name was used as a "household word" in a prefatory poem by T[om] B[rown], which is addressed "to his unknown Friend, Mr. *Henry Purcell*": "In thy Performance we with Wonder find | *Bassani*'s Genius to *Corelli*'s joy'nd." The entire poem has been reprinted in Burden, *Purcell Remembered*, 63–64.

15. North, *On Music . . . c.1695–1728*, xix–xx.

16. See GB-Ob, Ms. Mus. Sch. C.75. Corelli's op. 2 in GB-Ob, Ms. Mus. Sch. C.76 was copied by different hands, but (the signature of?) "Tho. Britton" was written on fol. 11. See *NG2*, s.v. "Britton, Thomas," by Michael Tilmouth and Simon McVeigh.

17. [Ned Ward], *The Secret History of Clubs* (London, 1709), 356.

18. The complete list is printed in John Hawkins, *A General History of the Science and Practice of Music* (London, 1853; reprint, New York: Dover, 1963), 792–93. Haym's name does not appear, but his sonatas could be among those listed anonymously. For example, nos. 71 and 74 include seven "sets of books of Sonatas by divers authors."

19. See John Hawkins, "The Life of Archangelo Corelli, the Celebrated Musical Composer" and "The General History and Peculiar Character of the Works of Archangelo Corelli," *The Universal Magazine of Knowledge and Pleasure* 60 (1777): 169–72; Owain Edwards, "The Response to Corelli's Music in Eighteenth-Century England," *Studia musicologica norvegica* 2 (1976): 51–96; Denis Arnold, "The Corellian Cult in England," in *Nuovi studi corelliani, Atti del secondo congresso internazionale, Fusignano, 5–8 September 1974*, ed. Giulia Giachin, Quaderni della Rivista italiana di musicologia, vol. 4 (Florence: L. S. Olschki, 1978), 81–89; Adriano Cavicchi, "Aspetti didattici ed elementi di prassi esecutiva nell'opera di Corelli," *Nuovi studi corelliani*, 91–104; Enrico Careri, "The Correspondence between Burney and Twining about Corelli and Geminiani," *Music & Letters* 72 (1991): 38–47; William Weber, *The Rise of Musical Classics in Eighteenth-Century England: A Study in Canon, Ritual, and Ideology* (Oxford: Clarendon Press, 1992), 79–89; Enrico Careri, "Francesco Geminiani e il culto inglese per Corelli," in *Studi corelliani 5: Atti del quinto congresso internazionale, Fusignano, 9–11 September 1994*, ed. Stefano La Via, Quaderni della Rivista italiana di musicologia, vol. 33 (Florence: L. S. Olschki, 1996), 347–77; and Careri, "The First Publications in England of Geminiani, Castrucci and Barsanti," *Studi Musicali* 27 (1998): 311–37. The presence of music by Corelli at concerts or theatrical events between 10 February 1703 and 5 April 1797 is recorded in *The London Stage, 1660–1800, Part 2: 1700–29*, ed. Emmett L. Avery; *Part 3: 1729–47*, ed. Arthur H. Scouten; *Part 4: 1747–76*, ed. George Winchester Stone, Jr.; and *Part 5: 1776–1800*, ed. Charles Beecher Hogan (Carbondale: Southern Illinois University Press, 1960–68). The dates are listed in Ben Ross Schneider, Jr., *Index to The London Stage, 1660–1800* (Carbondale: Southern Illinois University Press, 1979), 193, s.v. "Corelli."

20. Rudolf Rasch, "Estienne Roger and John Walsh: Patterns of Competition between Early-18th-Century Dutch and English Music Publishing," in *The North Sea and Culture (1550–1800)*, ed. Juliette Roding and Lex Heerma van Voss (Hilversum: Verloren, 1996), 396–407.

21. Michael Tilmouth, "A Calendar of References to Music in Newspapers Published in London and the Provinces (1660–1719)," *R. M. A. Research Chronicle* 1 (1961): 27 and 34.

22. Their advertisements are cited in nos. 31 and 41 in William C. Smith, *A Bibliography of the Musical Works Published by John Walsh during the Years 1695–1720* (London: The Bibliographical Society, 1948; reprint, 1968), 13–14 and 17.

23. For example, theatrical and instrumental "aires" predominate in Walsh's catalog of December 1703; see no. 140 in ibid., 41–45.

24. No. 63 in ibid., 22. The source was Giovanni Maria Bononcini's *Arie e correnti a trè, due violini e violone*, op. 12 (Bologna, 1678). On 16 June 1705, Walsh reprinted the collection as *Bononcini's Aires for Two Flutes and a Bass or Two Flutes without a Bass* (no. 178 in Smith, *A Bibliography of . . . the Years 1695–1720*, 56). For a comparison of the contents of the three editions, see William Klenz, *Giovanni Maria Bononcini of Modena: A Chapter in Baroque Instrumental Music* (Durham: Duke University Press, 1962), 59–61. In 1711, Luke Pippard printed *A Second Set of Bononcini's Aires, in Three Parts for Two Flutes and a Bass*, the source of which is Bononcini's *Ariette, correnti, gighe, allemande e sarabande*, op. 7 (Bologna, 1673).

25. Nos. 85 and 135 in Smith, *A Bibliography of . . . the Years 1695–1720*, 27 and 40.

26. Nos. 76, 129, 131, and 140 in ibid., 24–25, 39–40, and 44.

27. No. 119 in ibid., 36.

28. No. 128 in ibid., 39. The source was Albinoni's *Balletti a tre*, op. 3 (Venice, 1701). See Michael Talbot, *Tomaso Albinoni: The Venetian Composer and His World* (Oxford: Clarendon Press, 1990), 13 and 276.

29. No. 133 in Smith, *A Bibliography of . . . the Years 1695–1720*, 40. A copy is in GB-DRc, C27/2. The first twelve of its twenty-four dances are derived from Albinoni's "Balletti a cinque," according to Talbot, *Tomaso Albinoni*, 79–80 and 280. The next ten are derived from Gio. Battista Vitali's *Balletti, correnti, gighe, allemande e sarabande* (Bologna, 1668), according to Sandra Mangsen, "The 'Sonata da Camera' before Corelli: a Renewed Search," *Music & Letters* 76 (1995): 30. These ten dances are the ones in Vitali's op. 4, nos. 1, 4, 7–8, and 12 (see Mangsen, op. cit., 28). Ziani could thus have composed no more than the last two airs in the volume.

30. Such a function is clear in Nicola Matteis's four collections of airs (1676–85), because they are organized and labeled in terms of their difficulty. See Matteis, *Ayres for the Violin*, 4 parts, facsimile ed. (Ridgewood, N. J.: Gregg Press, 1966), and Peter Walls, "The Influence of the Italian Violin School in 17th-Century England," *Early Music* 18 (1990): 581.

31. See Lowell Lindgren, "Nicola Cosimi in London, 1701–1705," *Studi musicali* 11 (1982): 242–43.

32. Tilmouth, "A Calendar of References to Music," 49.

33. No. 125 in Smith, *A Bibliography of . . . the Years 1695–1720*, 38. In order to win his battle with Walsh, Vaillant, in an advertisement of 29 May 1703, said that a seventh solo would be given to buyers of Roger's edition. The copy in D-WD contains seven sonatas; see Zobeley, *Die Musikalien der Grafen von Schönborn-Wiesentheid*, part 1, vol. 1:126–27. According to Rasch, "Estienne Roger and John Walsh," 400–401 and 405–6, Walsh "pirated" sixty-five of Roger's publications.

34. Composers in Italy began to choose Roger as the first publisher for their works only in 1710; see Rudolf Rasch, "La famosa mano di Monsieur Roger: Antonio Vivaldi and His Dutch Publishers," *Informazioni e studi vivaldiani* 17 (1996): 89–90.

35. During the two years before he printed Haym's op. 1, he printed two collections of "free" sonatas by English composers: James Sherard's op. 1 (1701), which was discussed in the introduction to part 1, and William Corbett's *XII Sonate a tre, due violini e violoncello col basso per l'organo*, op. 1 (1702). Corbett's collection is discussed in Owain Edwards, "William Corbett's Instrumental Music," *Svensk tidskrift för musikforskning* 64 (1982): 9–17.

36. Francis Vaillant's advertisement for Visconti's op. 1, printed in *The Post-Man* for 29 April 1703, ends by declaring that Londoners "may be furnished with all sorts of Italian Musick Books" at his shop near Catherine Street in the Strand. His advertisements are exclusively for prints by Roger.

37. In his opp. 1–2, the only "modern" dance with chordal texture and four-bar phrases is the gavotta; there is no minuetto. This contrasts markedly with any volume that favors preclassical style, such as Martino Bitti's *Sonate a due, violino e basso, per suonarsi con flauto, o 'vero violino* (London, 1711). Each of its eight works consists of a prelude followed by three airs, and three of the works include both a gavotta and a minuetto. See nos. 396 and 401 in Smith, *A Bibliography of . . . the Years 1695–1720*, 119–21.

38. Both op. 1 and op. 2 use G major twice. Since op. 2 also repeats C major, G minor, and A minor, it lacks three keys found in op. 1, namely, B-flat major, D minor, and C minor.

39. In the ensuing discussion, all time signatures except **C** are listed before the tempo or title marking. The lack of a signature thus means it is **C**. There are more than a dozen shortcomings in the tabulations of time signatures, keys, and lengths provided for Haym's op. 2 in Angela Lepore, "La Sonata a tre in ambito corelliano," in *Intorno a Locatelli: Studi in occasione del tricentenario della nascita di Pietro Antonio Locatelli (1695–1764)*, ed. Albert Dunning, Speculum Musicæ, vol. 1 (Lucca: Libreria Musicale Italiana, 1995), 1:561–62. (NB: In references to sonata movements, a dot is preceded by an arabic sonata number and followed by a roman movement number.) No. 1.iv should be 11 + 27 measures, not 2 × 38 measures. No. 2.iv has $\frac{3}{4}$ only in the violin 1 partbook; $\mathbf{C}\frac{3}{4}$ is in the other two. No. 3.iii is in *Mi*-flat, not *Mi*. No. 5.ii has $\mathbf{C}\frac{3}{4}$ only in the violin 1 partbook; $\frac{3}{4}$ is in the other two. No. 5.iii is modulatory, from *re* to *sol* to *la*. No. 5.v is in *re*, not *Re*. No. 6.iii is modulatory, from *Mi*-flat to *do* to *sol* to *do* to *sol*. No. 7.iv has ¢ in the violin 2 partbook; **C** is in the other two. No. 8.v has "Da capo" at the end of the closing gavotta. No. 9.iv has $\mathbf{C}\frac{12}{8}$ in all parts. No. 11.iii is 8 + 8, plus

variation of 8 + 8. No. 12 has $\frac{3}{4}$ in the violone partbook; $\mathbf{C}\frac{3}{4}$ is in the violins. No. 12 is 25 × 4 + 2 measures.

40. They are discussed and listed in the critical report in each volume. See part 1, n. 25–26, and this volume, n. 12–13.

41. As reported in the introduction to part 1, Peter Allsop, *Arcangelo Corelli: New Orpheus of Our Times* (Oxford: Oxford University Press, 1999), 158, hears "Corellian" leapfrogging in Haym's no. 1.i and no. 1.iii, finds resemblances between Haym's no. 1.ii and Corelli's op. 3, no. 6, and op. 1, no. 11, and perceives "more than a passing similarity" between Haym's no. 1.iv and Corelli's op. 6, no. 4.

42. Perhaps Haym signified his focus on C minor by means of the key signature with two flats. Op. 2, no. 6, which is also in G minor, has a signature of one flat and does not focus on C minor.

43. Lepore, "La Sonata a tre in ambito corelliano," 560, lists "flauti [dolci]," that is, recorders, as the intended instruments, presumably because the word "traversi" is not given. It is given on the title page for the solo sonatas printed in part 1 of this edition.

44. It is the only trio sonata by Haym that has been commercially published. The fine edition by David Lasocki, which includes a bass realization by Walter Bergmann, was published by Hargail Press, New York, in 1978. The treble parts are labeled alto recorder 1 and 2 (with violin 1 and 2 given in parentheses) and the bass is labeled keyboard and violoncello (with viola da gamba given in parentheses). Bergmann's realization was made "with harpsichord or piano in mind."

45. The only eighth without a sounding note is the final one in measure 36, where hemiola occurs in the first treble part. Lasocki's edition marks each return of the subject in expositions 2–7 with angle brackets. Note that exposition 6 (mm. 30–31), which is in stretto, employs an altered version of the subject.

46. It is thus comparable to the ending of the closing $\frac{12}{8}$ Allegro in Corelli's op. 5, no. 3, in C major.

47. The dynamic markings in measures 9–11 and 13, which are given only in the violin 1 partbook, confirm that this was Haym's intent. If the second half is to agree with the first, the patterned figuration in measures 27–29 should be marked piano and the recapitulation in measures 30–31 should be marked forte.

48. Twelve events are listed in Hans Joachim Marx, "Die Musik am Hofe Pietro Kardinal Ottobonis unter Arcangelo Corelli," *Analecta Musicologica* 5 (1968): 166, s.v. "[Colombani]."

49. They are listed in Claudio Sartori, *I libretti italiani a stampa dalle origini al 1800* (Cuneo, 1990–94), Indici, 1:372, s.v. "Colombani."

50. Pitoni, *Notitia de' contrapuntisti e compositori di musica*, ed. Cesarino Ruini, Studi e testi per la storia della musica, vol. 6 (Florence: Leo S. Olschki, 1988), 343. According to Girolamo Colleoni, *Notizia degli scrittori più celebri che anno illustrato la patria loro di Correggio per ordine alfabetico disposti e colla breve indicazione de proprii scritti* [Guastalla, 1776], xiii, Colombani died instead from poisoning around 1735. This presumably incorrect reason for and date of death have been repeated, for example, by François Joseph Fétis, *Biographie universelle des musiciens*, 2d ed. (Paris, 1867–83), 2:338, and *NG2*, s.v. "Colombani, Quirino," by Angela Lepore. Colleoni's brief entry concerning Colombani has been reprinted in Lowell Lindgren, "Count Rudolf Franz Erwein von Schönborn (1677–1754) and the Italian Sonatas for Violoncello in His Collection at Wiesentheid," in *Relazioni musicali tra Italia e Germania nell'età barocca, Atti del VI Convegno internazionale sulla musica italiana nei secoli XVII–XVIII, Loveno di Menaggio (Como), 11–13 July 1995*, ed. Alberto Colzani et al. (Como: Antiquae Musicae Italicae Studiosi and Centro italo-tedesco Villa Vigoni, 1997), 288 n.

51. GB-Lbl, Ms. Add. 64965. On fol. 31 each of two movements is headed "Adagio dell Quirino Colombano." The first, consisting of 11 measures of $\frac{3}{4}$ in A minor, is from a sonata in C major. The second, consisting of 14 measures of $\frac{3}{2}$ that modulates from F-sharp minor to D minor, is from a sonata in D

major. Both feature chordal texture and employ hemiola passages.

52. It survives in D-WD, Ms. 896, pp. 61–64, and in I-Mc, Noseda Ms. M-30-7, and is discussed and edited in Lindgren, "Count Rudolf Franz Erwein von Schönborn," 288 and 299–302.

53. Nos. 166 and 283 and plate 14 in Smith, *A Bibliography of . . . the Years 1695–1720*, 53–54 and 90. A facsimile edition of *Select Preludes & Vollentarys for the Violin* was published in New York as Performers' Facsimiles, no. 164 (1996). The F major "Prelude by Sign^r Hyme" for flute has been published in *Preludes and Voluntaries for Treble Recorder Solo, 1708*, ed. Rene Colwell (London: Schott, 1950), 24.

54. The print is listed and described as Source C in the critical report.

55. The book is currently in US-NH, Beinicke Rare Book Library, Osborn Music MS 16. See Harold E. Samuel, "Johann Sigismond Cousser in London and Dublin," *Music & Letters* 61 (1980): 158–71, and Harold E. Samuel, "A German Musician Comes to London in 1704," *Musical Times* 122 (1981): 591–93.

56. In the edition of *Songs* published by John Walsh, the "Symphony or Overture" is given in a reduced score for a treble and figured bass. For editions by Walsh, see nos. 292–94 in Smith, *A Bibliography of . . . the Years 1695–1720*, 91–93.

57. The vignettes are reproduced in Adriano Cavicchi, "Prassi strumentale in Emilia nell'ultimo quarto del Seicento: flauto italiano, cornetto, archi," *Studi Musicali* 2 (1973): facing pp. 112 and 128.

58. Reproduced as plate 2 in Lindgren, "Nicola Cosimi," facing p. 237, and in Lindgren, "Italian Violoncellists and Some Violoncello Solos Published in Eighteenth-Century Britain," *Music in Eighteenth-Century Britain*, ed. David Wyn Jones (Aldershot, Hants, UK, and Burlington, Vt: Ashgate, 2000), 123.

59. Caricature by Pier Leone Ghezzi, reproduced as figure 14 in Stefano La Via, " 'Violone' e 'Violoncello' a Roma al tempo di Corelli: Terminologia, modelli organologici, techniche esecutive," *Studi corelliani* 4. La Via also reproduces the aforementioned depictions of cellists in prints by Jacchini and Cosimi (figs. 7 and 9) and reproduces five caricatures of cellists drawn by Ghezzi between 1742 and 1751 (figs. 15–19). All figures are placed between pp. 176 and 177.

60. See Lindgren, "Italian Violoncellists and Some Violoncello Solos," 137–38.

61. According to Tilmouth and Field, "Consort Music II: from 1660," 279, "in England the displacing of the bass viol by the cello in sonatas was perhaps not the least important consequence of the passion for Corelli."

62. North, *On Music . . . c.1695–1728*, 309 and 309 n.

63. Tilmouth, "A Calendar of References to Music," 14 and 41.

64. *NG2*, s.v. "Lenton, John," by Peter Holman.

65. Lenton, *The Gentleman's Diversion, or The Violin Explained* (London, 1693), 11 (which reappeared as *The Useful Instructor on the Violin* [London, 1702]). The copy is in the Cardiff Public Library, M.C.1.90. I am very grateful to Gillian Jones, Music Librarian at the University of Cardiff, who kindly provided me with a photocopy. It and its significance are described in Malcolm Boyd and John Rayson, "*The Gentleman's Diversion*: John Lenton and the First Violin Tutor," *Early Music* 10 (1982): 329–32.

66. This is the "French grip," which is described and illustrated in Mary Cyr, "Violin Playing in Late Seventeenth-Century England: Baltzar, Matteis, and Purcell," *Performance Practice Review* 8 (1995): 54–66.

67. This comes from "An Essay of Musicall Ayre" (ca. 1715–20) and is printed in North, *On Music . . . c.1695–1728*, 117–18.

68. See ibid, 100, for North's ordering of tempos and humours: "*adagio, grave, allegro, presto, prestissimo*; and for humour *andante, ricercata, affectuoso, maninconico* [melancholy], *cantabile*, and others dayly new." Some are briefly defined ibid., 123: "The *adagios* are designed for pure and pute [simple] harmony, for which reason measure of time is so litle regarded in

them. The *grave* comes neerer a sober conversation, and the *allegro* light and chirping. The *tremolo* is fear and suspicion, the *andante* is a walking about full of concerne, the *ricercata* is a searching about for somewhat out of the way; the *affectuoso* is expostulating, or *amour.*" See ibid., 182–86 and 188–96, and *Roger North's "The Musicall Grammarian 1728,"* 181–86 and 188–90, for a fuller discussion and exemplification of adagio, grave, allegro, and (only in *On Music*) andante.

69. See North, *On Music . . . c.1695–1728,* 111–12, for his identification of "the comon passions of joy and sorrow" with "the two different keys, termed sharp and flatt," i.e., major and minor. See *Roger North's "The Musicall Grammarian 1728,"* 170, for a similar statement: "Nothing is more materiall to be well understood by a learner then the difference in the air of notes which as keys carry a sharp or a flatt third; for the carracter of the musick depends on that distinction. The sharp belongs to triumph, mirth and felicity, and the flat to querelousness, sorrow and dejection; and it is a wonder that so small a change in the cours of the scale should have such glaring consequences."

70. For a discussion of fuges, see North, *On Music . . . c.1695–1728,* 179–80, and *Roger North's "The Musical Grammarian 1728,"* 180–81.

71. After his discussion of tempos, North, *On Music . . . c.1695–1728,* 197, declares that he "shall not medle in particular with divers other species brought into sonnatas, tho' comon to all other more trifling occasions, such as Gavotts, Courants, Giggs and the like, calculated for merry feasting and dancing; all which draw the air into a single upper part, and nothing but the measure allowed to divert the rest."

Plate 1. Nicola Francesco Haim, op. 2, middle of Sonata No. 11 in G major from the Violino primo partbook, p. 19. In this sonata, the part is labeled "Violino Solo." Reproduced by permission of the Library of Congress.

Plate 2. Nicola Francesco Haim, op. 2, middle of Sonata No. 11 in G major from the Violino secondo partbook, p. 19. In this sonata, a Violoncello replaces the Violino secondo. Reproduced by permission of the Library of Congress.

Plate 3. Nicola Haim, opening page of the second violoncello sonata in Milan, Conservatorio di Musica "Giuseppe Verdi," Noseda Ms. G-65-2, written by a Roman scribe, conjecturally around 1694. Reproduced by permission of the Biblioteca del Conservatorio di Musica "Giuseppe Verdi."

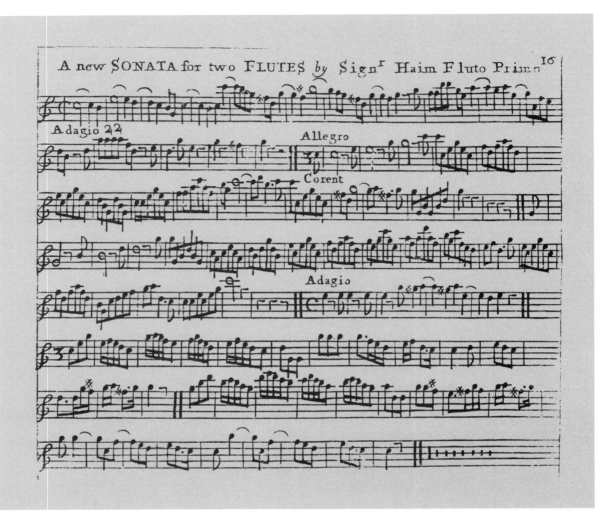

Plate 4. Sign^r Haim, Fluto primo part of "A new Sonata for two Flutes," in *Choice Italian and English Musick for Two Flutes, in which is contain'd the Overture of Pyrrhus and Demetrius, as also . . . Three Excellent New Sonata's and a Chacoone by Corelli, Nicolini Haim, Torelli, and Pez* (London, [1709]), 16. Only the Fluto primo part survives. Reproduced from the copy in the Mackworth Collection, belonging to Cardiff Public Library, but on permanent loan to the Music Department of Cardiff University. By permission of the Cardiff Public Library in Wales.

Sonate a tre, Op. 2

Dedication

Dedicate | *All'illustrissimo Signore* | Il Sig.^{re} Riccardo Edgcumbe.

Illustrissimo Signore

Mi crederei fortunatissimo, se coi caratteri Musicali della mia penna potessi pagare, Le tante obligationi; che tengo appresso di V.S. Illus.^{ma}; Ma questi sono troppo tenui, per contrabilanciar tante gratie: Non mi reputo pertanto indegno di scusa, mentre gli offro ciò che posso, non potendo ciò che devrei, e spero almeno, che presentandoli a V: S: Illus.^{ma}, scopriranno il desiderio, che ho di gradirgli, se non satisfaranno i mi debbiti, et mi daranno occasione di dedicarmi quale anbisco di essere

Londra li 15 ottobbre 1704.
Di V: S: Illus.^{ma}
                 Umilis.^{mo} et Oblig.^{mo} Servitore
                 Nicola Fran.^{co} Haim

Dedicated to the illustrious Sir, Mr. Richard Edgcumbe.

Illustrious Sir

I would consider myself most fortunate if, with the musical notes from my pen, I could recompense the many favors I have had from you, illustrious sir; but these [notes] are too meager to counterbalance the many favors. Do not regard them as unworthy, since I offer you what I can, not being able to give what I should. By presenting them to you, illustrious sir, I hope, at the very least, that they will reveal my wish to please you; though they will not satisfy my debts, they will provide me with an occasion to dedicate myself to what I aspire to be

London, 15 October 1704
Illustrious sir, your
                 Most humble and obliged servant,
                 Nicola Fran^{co} Haim

Sonata No. 1 in C Major
for Two Violins and Basso continuo

Gavotta. Allegro

8

Sonata No. 2 in D Major
for Two Violins and Basso continuo

Sonata No. 3 in G Minor
for Two Violins and Basso continuo

Sonata No. 4 in A Major
for Two Violins and Basso continuo

Sonata No. 5 in A Minor
for Two Violins and Basso continuo

Allegro

Sonata No. 6 in G Minor
for Two Violins or Two Flutes and Basso continuo

Sonata No. 7 in C Major
for Two Violins or Two Flutes and Basso continuo

Gavotta

Sonata No. 8 in F Major
for Two Violins or Two Flutes and Basso continuo

Giga. Allegro

Gavotta

Da capo

Sonata No. 9 in E Minor
for Two Violins or Two Flutes and Basso continuo

Sonata No. 10 in A Minor
for a Violin and a Violoncello and Basso continuo

44

Allemanda. Andante

Sonata No. 11 in G Major
for a Violin and a Violoncello and Basso continuo

Allemanda. Largo e puntato

Sonata No. 12 in G Major
for Two Flutes and Basso continuo

I-Mc, Noseda Ms. G-65-2

Sonata[?] in A Minor / E Minor
for Violoncello and Basso continuo

segue

Presto

Fine

Sonata in G Major
for Violoncello and Basso continuo

Fine

Sonata[?] in G Minor
for Violoncello and Basso continuo

Quirino [Colombani]

GB-Lbl, Add. Ms. 64965, fols. 11–13

Sonata in C Major
for Two Violins, Archlute, and Basso continuo

[Giovanni] Antonio Haim

Critical Report

Sources

Source A

Sonate a trè, cioè violini, flauti, violoncello e basso continuo per il cembalo, di Nicola Francesco Haim romano, op. 2, was dedicated by Nicola Franc.ᶜᵒ Haim to Sigʳᵉ Riccardo Edgcumbe on 15 October 1704, and was published in three partbooks "in Amsterdam per Estienne Roger, 1704." The page measurements are the same as those in op. 1 of 1703: after some trimming, each page is about 19.5 cm high by 24.6 cm wide, and each engraved image is 16.5 cm high by 20.2 cm long. Each partbook begins with the same two folios, which contain the title page and dedication. "Violino primo" and "Violino secondo" continue with eight staves of music on pages 1–21, and "Violone o leuto" continues with eight staves of music on pages 1–19. Centered at the top of each music page is a word or two that identifies the instrument. In the first partbook, "violino primo" appears on page 1, "violino" appears on even-numbered pages 2–18, "flauto" appears on page 20, "primo" appears on odd-numbered pages 3–15 and 21, and "solo" appears on pages 17 and 19 (as shown on plate 1). In the second partbook, "violino secondo" appears on page 1, "violino" appears on even-numbered pages 2–14, "violoncello" appears on pages 16–19 (as shown on plate 2), "flauto" appears on page 20, and "secondo" appears on odd-numbered pages 3–15 and 21. In the third partbook, "violone o leuto" appears on page 1, "violone" appears on even-numbered pages 2–18, and "o leuto" appears on odd-numbered pages 3–19. Each partbook ends with an unnumbered page headed "Indice," which lists each of the twelve sonatas, its instrumentation, and its page number. Nos. 1–5 are "Sonate per due violini e basso," nos. 6–9 are "Sonate proprie per due violini o per due flauti," nos. 10–11 are "Sonate a violino e violoncello con il basso continuo," and no. 12 is "Partite di Ciaccona per due flauti e basso." The engraver ended every movement with a double barline, i.e., with two vertical lines that span all five staff lines. At the end of the sonata, he added about six vertical lines that gradually decrease in length, until they end with a point on the middle line. They mark the end of a piece in a far simpler way than do the elaborate designs found in Haym's op. 1.

The three known exemplars are the following:

1. B-Bc, V 13.504. I have not seen this copy, but Paul Raspé, Bibliothécaire at the Conservatoire Royal de Bruxelles, kindly supplied a physical description. Each partbook is complete. Each was bound in boards during the nineteenth century. The only handwritten mark found within them is "Lott 17" on the title page of the part for "Violone o leuto." This conjecturally identifies the B-Bc copy with the one Haym owned at his death. Twenty-six numbered items or lots of "Musick-Books" are listed in *A Catalogue of the Large and Valuable Library of Books, lately belonging to the Learned and Ingenious* Antiquarian, *Mr.* Nicola Haym, *(Deceas'd.)* (London, 1730), 47. No. 17 is "Sonate e [*sic*] tre, cioè violini, flauti, violonc. d. Sign. Haym, Opera 2."

2. GB-Ob, Mus. Sch. E.510a–c. Older call numbers, which were written in pencil on each title page, have largely been erased: D.3.71 = 510a, D.3.72 = 510b, and D.3.73 = 574c. They continue the older numerical series found on Haym's op. 1 at GB-Ob, Mus. Sch. E.509a–c.[1] The pages in each part have been trimmed in an uneven manner to a height of about 17.8 cm and a width of about 22.4 cm. The opening and/or closing pages of each partbook have browned with age. The top of each one is very dirty. The smudges found within each book might have been caused by performers turning the pages with dirty fingers. Nine holes run from the top to the bottom at the middle of each opening (e.g., pp. 2–3, 4–5, 6–7, etc., are openings), and modern thread has been placed through these holes. Two folios (pp. 11–14) in the violin 2 partbook are loose, that is, no longer sewn together with the rest. The cardboard binding was presumably added in the twentieth century. No handwritten addenda were found in any partbook.

3. US-Wc, M351.H56Op.1.Case. As reported in volume 1, this call number includes both op. 1 and op. 2, and each bound partbook includes both prints. The brown suede bindings, which are described in volume 1, may well date from the eighteenth century. The beginning or ending of each partbook is a bit frayed and darkened by dirt. No handwritten addenda were found. The music was edited from this copy.

Source B

Three sonatas for violoncello in I-Mc, Noseda Ms. G-65-2 (olim 11.730). None of the three pieces in this manuscript has a title. On folios 1 and 3, "Del Sigʳ Nicola Haim" is placed at the upper right-hand corner of two four-movement pieces (see plate 3 for fol. 3). On the final page, folio 4v, "Del Sigʳ Quirino [Colombani]" is similarly placed before a two-movement piece. Someone later tried to erase "Haim" from folio 1 and "Quirino" from folio 4v; still later (perhaps in the nineteenth century), someone added "Nicola Deinl" at the upper left corner of folio 1. The pieces are therefore attributed to Deinl in the catalogue of the Biblioteca del Conservatorio di Musica "Giuseppe Verdi" in Milan. The four folios are about 21 cm high and 28.5 cm wide. Each includes five pairs of staves for unspecified instruments. The upper staff, which must be intended for violoncello, employs the bass or tenor clef, while the lower one, which is surely for basso continuo, uses the bass clef, but has no figuration. The musical scribe and the watermark, which is a fleur within two concentric circles with a V above, identify this as a Roman manuscript of around 1700.[2] This edition includes the two movements by Quirino, as well as the two pieces by Haym.

Source C

"A new Sonata for two Flutes by Sign.r Haim," *Choice Italian and English Musick for Two Flutes, . . . to which are added Three Excellent New Sonata's and a Chacoone by Corelli, Nicolini Haim, Torelli, and Pez. Note. That there are added Several Ariets of the New Opera [Clotilda] introduc'd with their Symphonys in this Edition which are not in the Former, and the Whole Much More Correct. All Engrav'd in a Fair Character* (London: I. Walsh, P. Randall, and I. Hare, [1709]), "Fluto Primo," p. 16. Copies of this partbook are extant at GB-CDp, M.C.1.82, and GB-Lbl, a.209.a/9. The former is shown as plate 4 in this volume and is listed as no. 201 in Sarah McCleave, *A Catalogue of Published Music in the Mackworth Collection* (Cardiff: University of Wales, Department of Music, 1996). The latter is listed as no. 295 in William C. Smith, *A Bibliography of the Musical Works Published by John Walsh during the Years 1695–1720* (London: The Bibliographical Society, 1948; reprint, 1968), 93. No flute 2 partbook is known to survive; if a bass partbook was published, it likewise does not survive. Walsh mentions a former edition on his title page. It was published by Luke Pippard and is known only from Pippard's complaint, published in *The Post-Man* for 30 April 1709, that Walsh had "reprinted and undersold" his "set of English and Italian Airs for two Flutes." Walsh presumably added the "New Sonata's and a Chacoone," as well as the "Ariets of the New Opera."

Source D

"Sonata dell [*sic*] Sig.r Antonio Haim," in GB-Lbl, Add. Ms. 64965, fols. 11–13. Each folio is about 32 cm high and 20 cm wide, and it includes four groups of four staves, labeled "violino primo," "violino secundo," "archleuto," and "basso continuo." The lowest two parts are written in the bass clef, are figured, and are identical, except when the archlute plays a few extra notes or plays the passages marked "solo" in movement 2. Haym's sonata is preceded by two pieces that have the same instrumentation, namely, a sinfonia and a sonata by "Gasparino." Haym's sonata is followed by about forty works (fols. 14–98), none of which includes a part for archlute. They are attributed to the Italians Bononcini, Caldara, Quirino

Colombani (discussed above), Carlo Marini, Stiffani (i.e., Steffani), and Torelli, and to the non-Italians Becker, Godfrey Finger, Francks, Morgan, and especially Pepusch. On folio 3, an apt title for the volume was written by the English musical scribe: "Musick (in Score) of two, three, four, five, and six parts, by severall authors, & likewise some Generall Rules of Composition, & for playing a through bass on the harpsicord." Another hand added: "by D.r Pepusch, & others." The scribe might be an unidentified student of Johann Christoph Pepusch (1667–1752), who had settled in London by 1698. Watermarks occur in the center of the folio-sized pages. One represents the arms of Amsterdam. It consists of a crowned shield; in its center the letter x appears vertically three times; and against its sides are lions rampant. The other watermark appears to be "K I S."[3] The binding is modern, but the original, tooled, suede leather covers have been feathered on. Folio 1v contains an early sale price, "£3.3" and the signature of an early owner, "J W Dodd, Dean's Yard, West[minste]r Abby." The last private owner identified himself on folio 2: "T[hurston] R[obert] D[art], purchased in Paignton, ab[ou]t 1943." The British Library purchased the manuscript at Sotheby's on 27 November 1987.

Editorial Methods

The current edition follows as closely as possible the 1704 set of parts for Haym's op. 2 and the manuscript scores for the sonatas that feature cello or archlute.[4] As in part 1 of this edition, titles for movements, tempo markings, clefs, key signatures, time signatures, slurs, ornaments, bass figures, dynamics, stem direction, and beaming have been altered minimally. But many cautionary accidentals have been eliminated, many tied notes have been replaced by their non-tied equivalents, and some brief rests in compound meters have been combined. The following comments will reiterate some general guidelines given in part 1, but will not recapitulate any of its citations to scholarly books and articles. The examples will all be drawn from the sources reproduced in this volume.

Tempo Markings

Tempo markings have been repositioned, in that they are always placed above the uppermost staff. Their usual location in the sources is below the staff in each engraved part of 1704 and below the uppermost staff in manuscript scores. A dance title precedes the tempo marking in ten fast movements of op. 2, namely, the second movements of nos. 6–11, and the fourth of nos. 1 and 8–10. A dance title occurs without a tempo marking in four fast movements, namely, op. 2, nos. 7.iv, 8.v, and 12, and Quirino's cello sonata, movement 2. The term "preludio," which heads the first movements of chamber sonatas in op. 1, is not found in op. 2.

Clefs and Signatures

In the sources, the treble parts are written in the treble clef, while the violoncello, archlute, and continuo parts are almost always in the bass clef. The continuo moves into the tenor clef only in op. 2, no. 6.iv, measures 37–39. The solo cello uses it occasionally in op. 2, nos. 10–11, and in Haym's Cello Sonata no. 2.ii, but employs it continuously in Quirino's movements. Solo passages for the archlute employ the tenor, alto, and soprano clefs in the second movement of Gio. Antonio Haym's sonata. Whenever such clefs appear in the sources, they have been retained in this volume.

The unaltered key signatures utilized in this volume include five that do not correspond to modern tonality, because they lack a sharp or a flat. All three pieces in G major (op. 2, nos. 11–12, and Cello Sonata no. 2) lack a sharp, while two of the pieces in G minor (op. 2, no. 6, and Quirino's sonata) lack a flat. The absence of an f♯ for op. 2, no. 11, can be seen in plates 1 and 2. This edition does not include the duplicate accidentals found in the signatures for four sonatas in the op. 2 partbooks. In these four, the accidentals found near the top of the staff are given again near the bottom. In other words, all three with one sharp in their key signature add f♯ on space 1, and one of them—in A major—also adds g♯ on line 2. The only piece with as many as two flats in its key signature adds an e♭ on line 1.[5]

Ten time signatures are found in the three sources. Seven of them—**c**, **¢**, ³⁄₂, ³⁄₄, ³⁄₈, ⁶⁄₈, and ¹²⁄₈—remain in use today. Three—**c**³⁄₂, **c**³⁄₄, and **c**¹²⁄₈—were already disappearing from use in Haym's day. The prefatory **c**, which presumably calls for a sober and reflective rendition of ³⁄₂, ³⁄₄, or ¹²⁄₈, is retained in this edition for all seven movements that employ it, even when **c** does not appear before ³⁄₄ in one or more partbooks.[6] The only conflict of **c** with **¢** occurs in no. 7.iv, a Gavotta in which **¢** occurs only in the violin 2 partbook. All except one of Haym's gavottes in opp. 1–2 are in **¢**, but he may have wanted no. 7.iv to be played relatively slowly, since it intermingles triplets with dotted-eighth plus sixteenth pairs. No. 5.vi, which has the same intermingling, is notated in **c**. Thus, **c** has been adopted in this edition.

Hemiola passages, which substitute three "imperfect" (i.e., undotted) values for two "perfect" (i.e., dotted) values, are somewhat obscured by the original notation. Hemiolas can be clarified by changing the meter from ⁶⁄₈ to ³⁄₄ or ³⁄₄ to ³⁄₂, but no such change was made in the sources represented herein. This edition has not superimposed any such change.[7] It has, however, clarified hemiolas in op. 2, no. 6.iv, measures 34–36 and 40–43, by eliminating the ties between the third and fourth eighth notes in ⁶⁄₈.

Articulation and Ornaments

Each note should be bowed individually unless it occurs within a slur. Slurs occur infrequently in op. 2, rarely in the cello sonata manuscript, and never in the archlute sonata manuscript. They are usually placed over pairs of sixteenths, eighths, or quarters. In order to achieve a consistent articulation, dashed slurs have been added by the editor of this volume. Triplets have slurs in only three finales, each of which has an unusual time signature. In two of them, no. 5.vi (notated in **c**) and 10.iv (a Giga in **c**¹²⁄₈), Haym placed the slurs over the first two

notes of a triplet. No. 10.iv is the only jig in op. 2 for which Haym provided any slurs.[8] Only in no. 7.iv (a Gavotta in **c**, as discussed above) did he place them over all three notes. His preference for slurs over the first two notes of a triplet has been noted in the critical report for part 1.

Ornaments are left almost entirely to the discretion of performers. None are specified in the manuscript sources. The only indications of them in op. 2 are the four + signs found in the violin 1 partbook for no. 6.iv, measures 25–26 and 37–38. In this edition, the + signs have been replaced by *tr*, the abbreviation for trill.[9] Performers in Haym's age were expected to add some embellishments within cadential formulas and during the repetition of each half of a dance. One "call" for florid embellishments may well be the fermatas found within and at the ends of slow movements. Indeed, each fermata might have been placed precisely where an ornamental flourish was to be played. Performers are advised to ignore most of the movement-ending fermatas and rests if they do not add a flourish.

Continuo Figures

Continuo figures are placed above the bass parts in the original sources for both Gio. Antonio Haym's sonata and Nicola Haym's op. 2. Identical figures are given above the archlute and basso continuo parts in Gio. Antonio's sonata and above the solo violoncello and violone parts in Nicola's op. 2, nos. 10–11. No bass figures are present in the manuscript containing sonatas for solo violoncello, and no figures have been added in this edition. In Gio. Antonio's sonata and in the current edition, the figures consist of numbers, accidentals, and numbers preceded by accidentals. In op. 2, an accidental is placed *after* a number whenever there is far less room for it *before* the number. Four pitch-raising symbols were added in op. 2: the numbers 2 and 4 have a vertical slash through their lengthened "tails," and the numbers 5 and 6 have a diagonal slash through their extended "tops." In this edition, a sharp or natural has replaced each of these symbols. A natural has also replaced any sharp that raises b♭ or e♭ by a half-step. Such changes in figuration are not listed in the critical notes.

Some figures that mark the resolution of a suspension have been moved forward in this edition, so that they will be placed directly under the resolution in an upper voice. A chord-player may choose to resolve a dissonance before a treble part resolves it on the last eighth or sixteenth note of a measure. Sometimes the chord-player alone must provide both the dissonance and its resolution.[10]

Dynamics

The only dynamics engraved in the source are Piano and Forte.[11] They have been reproduced in this edition as *piano* and *forte*. The most common marking by far specifies that the written-out reiteration of a final phrase must be played piano, as if it were an echo. This customary procedure is responsible for the only two dynamics in Haym's cello sonatas.[12] In op. 2, no. 8, each half of the

Allemanda and Giga ends with a piano marking for such a reiteration. In no. 5.v, two echoes occur in close succession. No. 10, the first work in which the violoncello—i.e., Haym—replaces violin 2, provides many illustrations of echoes followed by forte outbursts. In no. 10.i, three echoes are followed by forte cadences. No. 10.iii closes with an echo followed by a forte cadence. The first and second halves of no. 10.iv each close with two echoes followed by fortes.

Sudden outbursts also occur at the ends of slow movements in which an authentic cadence is followed by a series of three detached chords, v⁶–iv⁶–V or V⁶–vii°⁶/V–V. The first chord is marked forte and the second is marked piano. In part 1, there are ten examples of such detached-chord transitions and eight examples of sustained-chord transitions, which should presumably be played without a forte jolt at the beginning. In this volume, detached-chord transitions occur at the ends of eight movements, five of which are in op. 2, and all but one of which are first movements.[13] Sustained-chord transitions are found three times in Nicola's cello sonatas and ten times in his op. 2. Eight of them are placed at the ends of third movements.[14] In general, therefore, there is a dramatic, detached build-up to movement two and a mellow, sustained lead-in to movement four.

Stems and Beams

Within the sources, "modern" conventions already determined the direction of stems and—in most cases—the beaming of them. In the present volume, beams always encompass a dotted quarter note in $\frac{3}{8}$, $\frac{6}{8}$, and $\frac{12}{8}$. They usually encompass only a quarter note in ¢, ℂ, and $\frac{3}{4}$, but four eighths that occur at the beginning or end of a ¢ or ℂ measure are beamed together, as are six eighths that occur in $\frac{3}{4}$. In the sources, such large groups of notes are frequently broken into smaller ones, which are easier to engrave when large leaps are present. Indeed, when engraved leaps of an octave were beamed, the upper note often had a downward stem, while the stem for the lower one pointed upwards. The relatively few alterations in beaming are not listed in the critical notes.

Accidentals

The engraved prints contain many cautionary accidentals.[15] For example, when any part leaps an unusual interval, such as an augmented fourth or diminished fifth, one of the notes is customarily preceded by a cautionary accidental, which "confirms" the correctness of the interval.[16] Whenever a pitch that is preceded by a sharp, natural, or flat occurs two or more times within a measure, the accidental is repeated after the intervening note(s). Whenever a pitch recurs without such a cautionary accidental, the performer (and editor) should no longer observe the accidental.[17] The many cautionary accidentals found in the sources are not reproduced in this edition, and their presence is not mentioned in the critical notes.

Tied Notes

The op. 2 partbooks contain many ties between pairs of notes that occur within the same measure. The engraver seems to have visualized an imaginary barline in the middle of every measure of ℂ or ¢ time. Thus a dotted half note at the beginning of a measure was written as a half tied to a quarter note.[18] In addition, a half or dotted quarter note that began on beat 2 was written as a quarter tied to a quarter or to an eighth note.[19] Perhaps Haym provided his engraver with a copy that was handwritten in this manner. It had great practical value in his age, when one staff often ended with the first half of a measure, and another began with the second half.[20] Such writing in "half-measure notation" may also help to explain the existence of cautionary accidentals, some of which occur after the partition of a measure in the middle.[21] In op. 1, dotted note values occur together with tied notes in many passages. The latter are overwhelmingly predominant in op. 2. In the present edition, the "half-measure notation" with tied notes has been replaced, and the critical notes do not indicate when it occurs in the sources.

Critical Notes

The notes below describe rejected source readings. Pitch names use the system in which middle C = c'. The following abbreviations are used: Vn. = Violin; Fl. = Flute; B. = Basso continuo part for Violone, Violoncello, Lute, or Cembalo.

Sonate a tre, Op. 2

SONATA NO. 1 IN C MAJOR

Adagio. M. 14, Vn. 2 and B., fermata directly above beat 3.

SONATA NO. 2 IN D MAJOR

Allegro. M. 31, B., figure below fifth note.
Adagio. M. 2, B., fermata directly above beat 3.

SONATA NO. 3 IN G MINOR

Grave. M. 7, B., beat 3, "Forte." M. 8, B., beat 2, "Piano."

SONATA NO. 4 IN A MAJOR

Adagio. M. 8, B., note 1, figure 9 is preceded by an upward slash; it is not reproduced, because its meaning is unknown.
Allegro. M. 4, B., note 1, figure 9.

SONATA NO. 5 IN A MINOR

Allegro. M. 22, B., note 4, c (cf. m. 20). M. 23, B., beat 4, quarter rest.

SONATA NO. 6 IN G MINOR

Adagio. M. 8, B., note 1, figure flat after (not under) 6.
Grave. M. 3, Vn. 1, the tie between the half and quarter notes on b' is mistakenly extended to the ensuing c".

Sonata No. 7 in C Major

Allemanda. M. 1, B., figure 6 under note 2.
Gavotta. Signature is ¢ in Vn. 1 and B. and ¢ in Vn. 2.

Sonata No. 10 in A Minor

Grave. Tempo is Adagio in B. M. 2, B., note 2, sharp under figure 9–8.
Allemanda. M. 13, Vn., note 8, e″.
Giga. M. 7, B., rest 1, quarter.

Sonata No. 11 in G Major

Vivace. M. 16, B., "Da Capo" (rather than a written-out repeat of mm. 1–16).

Sonata No. 12 in G Major

Partite di Ciaccona. M. 102, B. (but not Fl. 1 or Fl. 2), repeat sign at the end of the measure.

I-Mc, Noseda Ms. G-65-2

Sonata in G Major

All°. M. 10, "da Capo" is written after the repeat sign at the end of the page (see plate 3); it presumably duplicates the meaning of the sign.
Adagio. M. 5, the pitches call for an unusual harmonization, perhaps ii–V⁶ in E major.

GB-Lbl, Add. Ms. 64965, fols. 11–13

Sonata in C Major by Antonio Haim

Allegro/Adagio. M. 5, beats 3–4, half rests in MS.
Allegro. Mm. 13–14, Vn. 2, note 3, a′. M. 16, archlute, note 1, the sharp is placed an octave above the note (because there is no space before it). M. 34, Vn. 2, note 5, d″.

Notes

1. According to Peter Ward-Jones, Music Librarian at the Bodleian, a previous owner may have written these numbers on the volumes.

2. One version of this typically Roman watermark is shown in Edward Heawood, *Watermarks, mainly of the 17th and 18th Centuries* (Hilversum: Paper Publications Society, 1950), no. 1591. The hand in I-Mc, Noseda Ms. G-65-2, is strikingly similar to that of the most important Roman copyist, Antonio Giuseppe Angelini. His many copies of works by Handel are listed and a page from one is reproduced in Keiichiro Watanabe and Hans Joachim Marx, "Händels italienische Kopisten," *Göttinger Händel-Beiträge* 3 (1987/1989): 195–234. Similar hands copied three Roman scores that have been reproduced in facsimile. B-Br, Ms. II.3962, which contains Alessandro Scarlatti's *Il Pompeo* (Rome, 1683), is reproduced in *Handel Sources: Materials for the Study of Handel's Borrowing*, ed. John H. Roberts (New York and London: Garland, 1986), vol. 6. US-Wc, M1528.B73.case, which contains Giovanni Bononcini's *La nemica d'Amore fatta amante* (Rome, 1693), is reproduced in *Cantatas by Giovanni Bononcini, 1670–1747*, ed. Lowell Lindgren (New York and London: Garland, 1985), 131–258. And GB-Abu, uncataloged Ms., fols. 57–68 and 105–111v, is reproduced in *Cantatas by Alessandro Scarlatti, 1660–1725*, ed. Malcolm Boyd (New York and London: Garland, 1986), 97–110. The latter two are vols. 10 and 13 in the series *The Italian Cantata in the Seventeenth Century*, ed. Carolyn Gianturco.

3. Cf. Heawood, *Watermarks*, nos. 403 (arms of Amsterdam with the letters KVS) and 414 (arms of Amsterdam with the letters KIK).

4. Since the part listed above as source C and reproduced as plate 4 is not edited in this volume, this source is not described in the ensuing notes.

5. The pieces with duplicate sharps are op. 2, nos. 2, 4, and 9. The only piece with duplicate flats is op. 2, no. 3, which is more often in C minor than in its tonic, G minor. See note 42 in the introduction to this volume.

6. All three partbooks have ¢³₂ for no. 5.iii, ¢³₄ for no. 3.iv, and ¢¹²₈ for nos. 9.iv and 10.iv. The following partbooks lack the ¢ before ³₄: violin 1 for no. 2.iv, violin 2 and violone for no. 5.ii, and violone for no. 12.

7. One could, for example, change ³₄ to ³₂ for the cadences in op. 2, no. 2.iv, mm. 9–10 and 38–39.

8. He provided none for no. 8.iv in ¹²₈ or no. 9.iv in ¢¹²₈.

9. They were equivalent, according to "A brief Discourse of the *Italian manner of Singing*," written by "an *English* Gentleman who had lived long in *Italy*": "Where this Mark + is set over a Note, the Trill is to be used." This gentleman's "Discourse" was printed in the fourth (1664) and later editions of John Playford, *An Introduction to the Skill of Musick*. It is found, for example, in the twelfth edition, corrected and amended by Henry Purcell in 1694 (ed. Franklin B. Zimmerman [New York: Da Capo Press, 1972], 16 and 90).

10. No one else, for example, provides the 7–6 called for in no. 5.vi, mm. 2 and 17, and in no. 10.i, m. 4. Five trills have been added to the violin parts in square brackets when no one provides the 4–3 called for in the figuration of op. 2. See no. 5.ii, m. 43; no. 7.ii, m. 9; no. 9.ii, m. 11; no. 10.iii, m. 23; and no. 12, m. 4. This is far fewer than the twenty-six comparable passages in op. 1. Trills have not been added in parallel passages that lack a 4–3 figuration, such as no. 7.ii, mm. 11 and 13–15, where performers may well add an embellishment. Trills have likewise been withheld from passages in op. 2, no. 10.i and ii, where the figuration is 4–3 but the solo violin plays 6–5. See no. 10.i, mm. 6, 7, 12, 14, 15, and 17, and 10.ii, mm. 13 and 14.

11. The abbreviations pia. and for., which are common in Haym's op. 1, appear only once in op. 2: in no. 7.i, violone, mm. 16–17.

12. No. 1.iv, m. 14, and no. 2.ii, m. 20.

13. The eight are Gio. Antonio's sonata, movements 1 and 2, Nicola's second cello sonata, movement 1, and op. 2, nos. 1.i, 5.i, 7.i, 9.i, and 11.i.

14. The thirteen are in the first cello sonata, movement 3; the second cello sonata, movements 2 and 3; and op. 2, nos. 1.iii, 2.ii, 3.iii, 4.i, 6.i, 6.iii, 7.iii, 8.iii, 9.iii, and 10.i. The forte marking given only in the violone part for no. 3.iii, m. 7, is presumably incorrect.

15. They also contain an accidental before or above the *mostra* or "direct" at the end of a staff whenever the note that begins the next staff is preceded by an accidental. This is true of Haym's opp. 1–2, his editions of Corelli's opp. 1–5, and the

VI Sonate da camera. One example is the sharp on the penultimate staff of plate 1.

16. A few such accidentals have been preserved in this volume. See, for example, op. 2, no. 6.iv, violin 2, m. 45, notes 4–5. In no. 9.iii, violin 2, m. 3, a sharp already in the key signature is given again to "confirm" the augmented fourth.

17. For examples in op. 2, see violin 1 in no. 4.ii, m. 3, note 6 (cf. m. 28, note 6); violone in no. 6.ii, m. 10, note 8, and in no. 12, mm. 29 and 30, note 8; and flute 2 in no. 12, m. 30, note 7. See also Cello Sonata no. 1.i, solo part, m. 7, note 8.

18. See, for example, violin 1, no.1.i, m. 2, and no. 1.iv, mm. 18–19 and 22–23; violin 2, no. 1.i, mm. 7–9, and no. 1.iv, mm. 1–2, 12–13, 16–17, 20–21, and 24–25; and violin 1 and violone, no. 6.iii, m. 10.

19. For examples of quarters tied to quarters, which are legion in op. 2, see violone, no. 1.i, mm. 3 and 5; violin 1, no. 1.i, mm. 1 and 6, and no. 1.ii, mm. 7, 16, 19, 20, and 30; and violin 2, no. 1.ii, mm. 4–5, 8, 11, 24–25, and 35–36. For examples of quarters tied to eighths in op. 2, see no. 4.iii, violin 2, mm. 3 and 6–7, and violone, m. 12; and see no. 6.i, violin 1, mm. 5–6. In no. 6.ii, mm. 2–8, the violins play many quarters tied to eighths in alternation. Six of the dotted eighths begin on strong rather than weak beats, but even they (with the exception of violin 1, m. 5, beat 3) are written as tied rather than dotted notes.

20. For examples of ties that began with the half-measure at the end of one staff and ended with the half-measure at the beginning of the next, see violin 1 for no. 1.ii, m. 20, no. 1.iv, m. 19, and no. 2.ii, m. 32; and violin 2 for no. 2.ii, m. 7.

21. For examples in op. 2, see violin 1 for no. 8.iii, m. 9; violin 2 for no. 9.iv, m. 13; violoncello (in the violin 2 partbook) for no. 10.iv, m. 10, and no. 11.i, m. 13. See also Cello Sonata no. 1.i, solo part, m. 10.